Improving Your Vocabulary

Mildred C. Carter
Dorothy H. Dlugacz

Monarch Press

Copyright © 1980 by Mildred C. Carter and Dorothy H. Dlugacz

Published by Monarch Press
A Simon & Schuster Division of
Gulf & Western Corporation
Simon & Schuster Building
1230 Avenue of the Americas
New York, New York 10020

Monarch Press and colophon are trademarks of Simon
& Schuster, registered in the U.S. Patent and Trade-
mark Office.

Designed by Irving Perkins
Manufactured in the United States of America

10 9 8 7 6 5 4 3 2

ISBN 0-671-18432-6

Contents

Preface

Words! Words! Words! Have you ever said to yourself:

> Why bother to learn more words?
> How can knowing more words help me?

The answer is simple. Words are the way we communicate with each other. Do you want to convince people that your ideas are right? Do you want to persuade people to do things your way? There's an easy way to do it—with words. The more words you know, the more forceful you can be.

In addition, words help you to understand others better. They help you to get the message quickly and to react intelligently. Words are the keys to accurate thinking. Therefore, if your vocabulary is limited, your ability to think and to communicate is limited. To put it briefly, a large vocabulary can be very helpful to you.

How can you increase your vocabulary? This book describes the skills you need and gives you practice in using them. In the process you will learn many helpful words in a painless way.

What are these skills? First among them is the skill of recognizing CONTEXT CLUES. This means using information located within the sentence or in the surrounding sentences to learn the meaning of unfamiliar words.

Second is the skill of recognizing STRUCTURAL CLUES. This means understanding the various parts of a word, what these parts mean, and how these parts are put together.

The final skill is the ability to locate words in a dictionary and to select the meaning that makes sense in a given sentence.

Like developing skills in a sport, developing skills in vocabulary requires practice. This book will provide you with that practice, but you will have to contribute a little bit more. You don't go out for a sport unless you're interested; and because you're interested, you practice and become more skillful.

The same is true of vocabulary development. First you have to renew your curiosity about people and places and things. Then you'll be interested in the

1

words that describe them. You'll become a collector. It's the collecting and the practice that develop the skill.

Words used in newspapers, on TV, and on the radio are the words you'll find in this book. Start collecting them and start developing your vocabulary skills.

You and Keys for Communication

Could you explain to a person learning English what the word SPRING means? Would you say it is a season of the year or a source of water or something that stretches?

SPRING means, of course, all of these things. Like many words, it has many meanings—MULTIPLE MEANINGS. But it has no exact meaning until it is used in a sentence. This sentence is the CONTEXT and provides clues to the meaning of a word. These clues are called CONTEXT CLUES.

Practice One:
Context Clues— SPRING

Underline the words that help you understand the meaning of SPRING in each of the following sentences.

1. Weeds seem to SPRING up more quickly than flowers.
2. This SPRING water is cold.
3. SPRING is my favorite season of the year.
4. The door won't close because the SPRING is broken.
5. Did your car radiator SPRING a leak?

Did you underline the following words?

1. WEEDS and FLOWERS. You know they both grow.
2. WATER and COLD
3. SEASON OF THE YEAR
4. DOOR WON'T CLOSE and perhaps BROKEN
5. RADIATOR and LEAK

Practice Two:
Definitions— SPRING

Next to each definition below, write the number of the sentence in Practice One that uses the word SPRING in this special way.

Definitions:

_____ **A.** a season of the year

_____ **B.** a source of water coming from the ground

_____ **C.** a device that regains its original shape after being stretched

_____ **D.** to grow rapidly

_____ **E.** to develop

The answers are A-3, B-2, C-4, D-1, and E-5. How did you know the exact meaning? Some of the words in each sentence acted as clues—CONTEXT CLUES.

CONTEXT CLUES can take the form of a DEFINITION (or restatement), an EXAMPLE, a COMPARISON, or a CONTRAST. Let's examine some of these types of context clues.

The following sentence contains a DEFINITION: The DEROGATORY comment expressed his low opinion of my idea. The clue is <u>low opinion</u>; DEROGATORY means <u>expressing a low opinion</u>.

Sometimes the context lists EXAMPLES to help you understand the meaning of an unfamiliar word. Notice the examples that illustrate the quality COMPASSION.

The stranger showed COMPASSION by helping the injured man. First he applied a pressure bandage to the bleeding wound. Then he covered the shivering man with a blanket.

Here the meaning of COMPASSION, the quality of sympathy, is made clear by the actions taken to help the injured man.

Another type of context clue is COMPARISON. For example, if you did not previously know the meaning of CIRCUITOUS, it becomes plain because of the comparison in the following sentence: The path is as CIRCUITOUS as a corkscrew.

A final type of context clue is a CONTRAST. This type of clue stresses the difference between things. How does the word ACQUIESCENT become clear in the following sentence? The child's behavior was ACQUIESCENT; he offered no objections to the plan. The contrasting expression *no objections* indicates that the child agreed quietly.

These samples are good additions for your word bank. Practice their pronunciation.

derogatory	de ROG a to ry
compassion	com PAS sion
circuitous	cir CU i tous
acquiescent	ac qui ES cent

To summarize, many words have MULTIPLE MEANINGS. CONTEXT CLUES help us to know the exact meaning and to understand the message.

Practice Three:
**Context Clues—
BASE**

Underline the words that help you understand the meaning of BASE in each of the following sentences.

1. The BASE of the tree is surrounded by fallen leaves.
2. Camp Pendleton is the BASE from which these marines receive their ammunition.
3. The marble BASE supported a bronze figure of John F. Kennedy.
4. The main ingredient for this paint is the oil BASE.
5. The player ran toward second BASE as soon as the batter swung.

Practice Four:
Definitions

Next to each definition below write the number of the sentence in Practice Three that uses the word BASE in this special way.

_____ **A.** the thing upon which something rests

_____ **B.** the main ingredient of something

_____ **C.** a place of safety in a ballgame

_____ **D.** a source of supply; headquarters

_____ **E.** the lowest part; the bottom

Practice Five:
Word Families

BASE is also used as a combining form. We are all familiar with baseball, base hit, baseline, and basement, but how about BASEBOARD, BASE PAY, BASEBORN, BASE EXCHANGE and BASELESS? Underline the CONTEXT CLUES which help you understand what each CAPITALIZED word means.

1. The rumor that we were getting a raise proved BASELESS. We didn't get any additional money.
2. The sailors bought their supplies at the BASE EXCHANGE because the prices were lower.
3. We installed a BASEBOARD to cover the crack between the floor and the wall.
4. His BASE PAY was $200.00 a week.
5. He was labeled BASEBORN because he was an illegitimate child.

Practice Six:
Definitions

Next to each definition below write the CAPITALIZED word in Practice Five that is defined. A clue is given at the end of each definition.

_____ **1.** a strip of board covering the line where the wall meets the floor (b-b-)

_____ **2.** the regular rate of pay not including overtime (b-p-)

_____ **3.** a post exchange or government store at a naval or air force base (b-e-)

_____ **4.** born to people not married to each other (b-b-)

_____ **5.** not factual, groundless (b-l-)

Now that you've been introduced to the use of context clues, here's some practice plus an opportunity to increase your vocabulary.

Words in the English language can be classified according to their use in sentences. NOUNS are used to identify people, places, things, emotions, and ideas.

Practice Seven:
Context Clues—
Nouns

Underline the CONTEXT CLUES that help you understand the meaning of each CAPITALIZED word.

1. After losing the sale, his CHAGRIN was obvious because of the annoyed look on his face.
2. In DEFERENCE to her business experience, we respected and followed her suggestion.
3. He showed DISCRETION by avoiding temptation and making a wise decision.
4. His ECCENTRICITY is that he will not ride in an elevator.
5. Her FINESSE in helping others work well together is her greatest skill.

Did you underline the following? 1. annoyed look, 2. respected and followed, 3. wise decision, 4. the entire example, 5. skill.

Practice Eight:
Definitions—Nouns

Write the CAPITALIZED word in Practice Seven that best matches each definition. If you need help, reread the original sentences for CONTEXT CLUES. A clue is given at the end of each definition.

Words	*Definitions*
_____	**1.** polite respect for others (def-)
_____	**2.** skillful handling of something (f-)
_____	**3.** not usual or normal behavior; peculiarity, oddity (e-)
_____	**4.** the power to make wise decisions; good judgment (dis-)
_____	**5.** a feeling of annoyance because one has been disappointed; irritation (c-)

Practice Nine:
Completion—Nouns

From the word list select the word needed to complete each of the following sentences. Look for the CONTEXT CLUES. These will tell you which word to use.

Word List: chagrin, deference, discretion, eccentricity, finesse.

1. His _____ is that he will not make any decisions on Friday, the thirteenth.
2. To her _____ she didn't get the job because her application was filed late.
3. His greatest skill is his _____ in settling labor problems.
4. We stand for the President of the United States out of _____ _____ for his office.
5. She showed _____ when she decided to put her money in a savings bank.

Practice Ten:
Context Clues— More Nouns

<u>Underline</u> the CONTEXT CLUES that help you understand the meaning of each CAPITALIZED word.

1. Although he is an intelligent person, he dislikes working. This INDOLENCE prevents his getting jobs finished on time.
2. She could not believe that she had won the lottery. Her INCREDULITY showed in her expression.
3. His PESSIMISM made him always expect the worst to happen.

4. The employee did not get the promotion he had worked so hard for. His RANCOR was obvious in the bitter tone of his voice.

5. The SERENITY of the meeting was broken by a violent argument.

Did you underline the following? 1. dislikes working, 2. could not believe, 3. expect the worst to happen, 4. bitter tone, 5. broken by a violent argument.

Practice Eleven:
Definitions—More Nouns

Write the CAPITALIZED word in Practice Ten that best matches each definition. A clue is given at the end of each definition.

Words	*Definitions*
_____	**1.** unable to believe; doubt, disbelief (inc-)
_____	**2.** the tendency to see only the bad side and to expect the worst; gloominess (p-)
_____	**3.** calmness, peacefulness (s-)
_____	**4.** a dislike of work; laziness (ind-)
_____	**5.** hatred, bitterness (r-)

Practice Twelve:
Completion—More Nouns

From the word list select the word needed to complete each of the following sentences. Look for the CONTEXT CLUES. These will tell you which word to use.

Word List: indolence, incredulity, pessimism, rancor, serenity.

1. The _____ of the group made them give up.

2. The _____ of the quiet evening was destroyed by a howling thunderstorm.

3. The boxer preferred sleep to roadwork. This _____ cost him the next fight.

4. He showed his _____ about getting no raise by refusing to work for the rest of the day.

5. The runner couldn't believe how quickly she had circled the track. Her _____ showed on her face.

Practice Thirteen:
Using the Nouns

Now can you use these nouns? Write the CAPITALIZED word that correctly answers each question.

_____ 1. Do you show DEFERENCE or RANCOR to older people?

_____ 2. Would RANCOR or INCREDULITY show on your face if you won a prize?

_____ 3. Would a thunderstorm spoil the PESSIMISM or SERENITY of a quiet evening?

_____ 4. Would PESSIMISM or SERENITY make a person feel unhappy and miserable?

_____ 5. If you were annoyed and upset by something, would CHAGRIN or SERENITY show on your face?

_____ 6. Do you use ECCENTRICITY or DISCRETION when you have to make an important decision?

_____ 7. If a bad call cheated your team out of a win, would your voice show RANCOR or DEFERENCE?

_____ 8. Would you use RANCOR or FINESSE in trying to settle an argument?

_____ 9. If you are afraid of the dark, is this an ECCENTRICITY or a SERENITY?

_____ 10. If you dislike working, would you be showing INDOLENCE or DEFERENCE?

Practice Fourteen:
Review of Nouns

You are given the definition. Has word A, B, or C been defined? Write the defined word on the line.

_____ 1. the tendency to see only the bad side and to expect the worst
A. rancor   B. pessimism   C. serenity

_____ 2. hatred, bitterness
A. rancor   B. incredulity   C. indolence

———————————————— **3.** unable to believe; doubt

A. finesse   B. chagrin   C. incredulity

———————————————— **4.** a polite respect for others

A. deference   B. pessimism   C. rancor

———————————————— **5.** not usual or normal behavior

A. eccentricity   B. serenity   C. discretion

———————————————— **6.** calmness, peacefulness

A. rancor   B. serenity   C. chagrin

———————————————— **7.** the power to make wise decisions

A. indolence   B. pessimism   C. discretion

———————————————— **8.** a dislike of work

A. finesse   B. incredulity   C. indolence

———————————————— **9.** skillful handling of something

A. finesse   B. eccentricity   C. rancor

———————————————— **10.** a feeling of annoyance because one has been disappointed

A. deference   B. chagrin   C. finesse

A group of words which help us to express our ideas more vividly and exactly is ADJECTIVES. These are words such as *tall, thoughtful, intelligent,* and *industrious.* They are used with nouns. For example, a tall man; a thoughtful person; an intelligent, industrious human being.

Practice Fifteen:
**Context Clues—
Adjectives**

Here are some adjectives that describe people. Underline the CONTEXT CLUES that help you understand the meaning of each CAPITALIZED word.

1. The reporter and the photographer were COMPATIBLE workers. They never argued over any assignments they were given.
2. The apprentice was a DOCILE worker. She accepted all instructions without question.
3. The office manager was DOGMATIC. He would not listen to suggestions from others.
4. The new vice president was so ELATED about her promotion that she decided to celebrate.
5. A salesperson must be GREGARIOUS and not a loner.

Did you underline the following? 1. never argued, 2. accepted all—without question, 3. would not listen to suggestions from others, 4. decided to celebrate, and 5. not a loner.

Practice Sixteen:
**Definitions—
Adjectives**

Write the CAPITALIZED word in Practice Fifteen which best matches each definition. A clue is given at the end of each definition.

Words	*Definitions*
_____	1. teachable, obedient, easily managed (doc-)
_____	2. likes being with other people; sociable (g-)
_____	3. able to get along well with others; agreeable (c-)
_____	4. joyful, in high spirits (e-)
_____	5. tending to give orders and opinions in a superior manner; dictatorial (dog-)

Practice Seventeen:
**Completion—
Adjectives**

From the word list select the word needed to complete each of the following sentences. Look for the CONTEXT CLUES that will tell you which word to use.

Word List: compatible, docile, dogmatic, elated, gregarious.

1. She is a very _____ person who likes people and enjoys parties.

2. We are _____ workers. We rarely have a disagreement.

3. I was _____ to learn that I had won the prize.

4. The child is _____ , quiet, and manageable.

5. A _____ person will not consider ideas offered by others.

Practice Eighteen:
**Context Clues—
More Adjectives**

Underline the CONTEXT CLUES which help you understand the meaning of each CAPITALIZED word.

1. One salesman is very LOQUACIOUS. He would rather talk than write up orders.
2. We knew the employer was IMPARTIAL when she gave the position to a stranger and not to her son.
3. The PENSIVE man was trying to remember where he had made his mistake.
4. The producer begged the actress to accept the TV job. She, however, was PERVERSE and refused.
5. The secretary's boss was SULLEN. He would not answer any questions about losing the advertising account.

Did you underline the following? 1. talk, 2. gave the position to a stranger and not to her son, 3. trying to remember where he had made his mistake, 4. begged—refused, and 5. would not answer any questions.

Practice Nineteen:
**Definitions—More
Adjectives**

Write the CAPITALIZED word in Practice Eighteen that best matches each definition. A clue is given at the end of each definition.

Words	*Definitions*
_____	1. silent and gloomy because of bad mood (s-)
_____	2. tending to be too talkative (l-)
_____	3. determined to do only what one wants to do; stubborn (per-)
_____	4. not taking sides; fair (im-)
_____	5. in deep thought, frequently about something sad; thoughtful (pen-)

Practice Twenty:
**Completion—More
Adjectives**

From the word list select the word needed to complete each of the following sentences. Look for the CONTEXT CLUES that will tell you which word to use.

Word List: impartial, loquacious, pensive, perverse, sullen.

1. When the child was angry he became _____ and refused to talk.

2. The salesman was so _____ I thought he'd run out of breath.

3. When Tom's suggestions were turned down, he became _____ and refused to take any further part in the discussion.

4. The prisoner was hoping that his case would be heard by an _____ judge.

5. She was thinking about her serious problem and was very _____.

Practice Twenty-One:
Using the Adjectives

Now can you use these adjectives? Write the CAPITALIZED word that correctly answers each question.

_____ **1.** Would a PENSIVE person or a GREGARIOUS person like to be alone?

_____ **2.** Would an ELATED person or a SULLEN person be silent and angry?

_____ **3.** Would a LOQUACIOUS person or a PENSIVE person like to give a speech?

_____ **4.** Should people try to be COMPATIBLE or PERVERSE?

_____ **5.** Would you be ELATED or SULLEN about good news?

_____ **6.** Is a SULLEN or a DOCILE person pushed around easily?

_____ **7.** Does a COMPATIBLE person or a PERVERSE person want only his own way?

_____ **8.** Would a GREGARIOUS person or a DOGMATIC person probably have a lot of friends?

_____ **9.** Should a judge be DOGMATIC or IMPARTIAL?

_____ **10.** Would a DOGMATIC person or a COMPATIBLE person expect to give all the orders?

Practice Twenty-Two:
Review of Adjectives

You are given the definition. Has A, B, or C been defined? Write the defined word on the line.

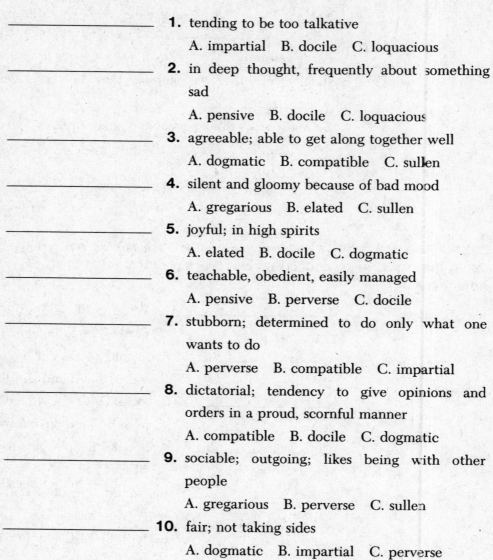

_____ **1.** tending to be too talkative

A. impartial   B. docile   C. loquacious

_____ **2.** in deep thought, frequently about something sad

A. pensive   B. docile   C. loquacious

_____ **3.** agreeable; able to get along together well

A. dogmatic   B. compatible   C. sullen

_____ **4.** silent and gloomy because of bad mood

A. gregarious   B. elated   C. sullen

_____ **5.** joyful; in high spirits

A. elated   B. docile   C. dogmatic

_____ **6.** teachable, obedient, easily managed

A. pensive   B. perverse   C. docile

_____ **7.** stubborn; determined to do only what one wants to do

A. perverse   B. compatible   C. impartial

_____ **8.** dictatorial; tendency to give opinions and orders in a proud, scornful manner

A. compatible   B. docile   C. dogmatic

_____ **9.** sociable; outgoing; likes being with other people

A. gregarious   B. perverse   C. sullen

_____ **10.** fair; not taking sides

A. dogmatic   B. impartial   C. perverse

This final group of words describes certain specific actions. These words are VERBS. They are words such as WALK and TALK. The word endings S, ED, and ING can be added to many verbs. For example: I walk. He walks. Yesterday he walked. He is walking.

Practice Twenty-Three:
Context Clues—Verbs

Underline the CONTEXT CLUES which help you understand the meaning of each CAPITALIZED word.

1. The company is trying to ACCRUE enough money to enlarge its plant.
2. I CONCUR with your opinion and agree to support your position at the meeting.
3. We will have to DEFER making a decision until we gather more information about the problem.
4. The bookkeeper must locate the error and RECTIFY it so that the records are correct.
5. I will have to RETRACT my offer to buy the land because I do not have enough money for the purchase.

Did you underline the following words? 1. enough money to enlarge its plant, 2. agree and possibly support your position at the meeting, 3. gather more information about the problem, 4. locate the error—so that the records are correct, and 5. I do not have enough money for the purchase.

Practice Twenty-Four:
Definitions—Verbs

Write the CAPITALIZED word in Practice Twenty-Three that best matches each definition. A clue is given at the end of each definition.

Words	*Definitions*
_____	**1.** withdraw; take back (ret-)
_____	**2.** postpone; put off (d-)
_____	**3.** agree; have similar opinion (c-)
_____	**4.** collect; grow in amount (a-)
_____	**5.** correct (rec-)

Practice Twenty-Five:
Completion—Verbs

From the word list select the word needed to complete each of the following sentences. Look for the CONTEXT CLUES that will tell you which word to use.

Word List: accrue, concur, defer, rectify, retract

1. I told the truth. I will not _____ my statement.
2. I will _____ my decision until tomorrow.
3. How much interest will I _____ by the end of the year?
4. I do not disagree. I _____ with your explanation of the problem.
5. I will _____ the error in addition at once.

Practice Twenty-Six:
**Context Clues—
More Verbs**

One last practice on CONTEXT CLUES. This is a particularly interesting group of verbs because they all have a similar ending—ATE. <u>Underline</u> the CONTEXT CLUES which help you understand the meaning of each CAPITALIZED word.

1. To ALLEVIATE the strain caused by all the extra work, the company hired another secretary.
2. The office manager ALLOCATES the work each morning so that each computer operator has an equal work load.
3. The union refused to CAPITULATE and continued to fight for a better contract.
4. This machine COLLATES the pages of a book so that they are in numerical order.
5. The law MANDATES that income tax be withheld from each employee's pay.

Did you underline the following words? 1. extra work, hired another secretary, 2. so that each computer operator has an equal work load, 3. refused—continued to fight, 4. pages of a book—numerical order, and 5. law—income tax be withheld from each employee's pay.

Practice
Twenty-Seven:
**Definitions—More
Verbs**

Write the CAPITALIZED word in Practice Twenty-Six that best matches each definition. A clue is given at the end of each definition.

Words	*Definitions*
_____	1. yield, give up (cap-)
_____	2. divides, distributes (allo-)
_____	3. officially orders or commands (m-)
_____	4. make something less hard to bear; lessen, relieve (alle-)
_____	5. arranges in correct order (co-)

Practice Twenty-Eight:
**Completion—More
Verbs**

From the word list select the word needed to complete each of the following sentences. Look for the CONTEXT CLUES that will tell you which word to use.

Word List: alleviate, allocate, capitulate, collate, mandates.

1. The law _____ that each employee gets at least the minimum wage.

2. Please _____ these papers so that they are in alphabetical order.

3. She will _____ the work so that each person has the same amount.

4. The fighter refuses to _____ even though his eye is swollen shut.

5. He took an aspirin to _____ the pain.

Practice Twenty-Nine:
Using the Verbs

Write the CAPITALIZED word that correctly answers each question.

_____ 1. Would you ALLEVIATE or COLLATE the pages of a report?

_____ 2. In a savings bank does money ACCRUE or MANDATE interest?

_____ 3. Would you expect a salesclerk to COLLATE or RECTIFY an error?

_____ 4. Would you do something to ALLOCATE or to ALLEVIATE the pain of a headache?

_____ 5. Does the government MANDATE or COLLATE taxes?

_____ 6. If you regret a remark you have made, would you RETRACT it or DEFER it?

_____ 7. Would an army COLLATE or CAPITULATE when it could no longer fight?

_____ 8. Do you DEFER or COLLATE work that you don't like to do?

_____ 9. Do you ALLOCATE or CAPITULATE your money in a budget?

_____ 10. When you agree, do you DEFER or CONCUR?

Practice Thirty:
Review of Verbs

You are given the definitions. Has word A, B, or C been defined? Write the defined word on the line.

_____   **1.** make something such as pain less hard to bear

        A. accrue B. alleviate C. collate

_____   **2.** officially orders or commands

        A. capitulate B. allocate C. mandate

_____   **3.** put off; postpone

        A. concur B. retract C. defer

_____   **4.** give up; yield

        A. capitulate B. accrue C. collate

_____   **5.** have similar opinion; agree

        A. defer B. concur C. rectify

_____   **6.** grow in amount; collect

        A. accrue B. defer C. retract

_____   **7.** arrange in correct order

        A. alleviate B. collate C. defer

_____   **8.** take back; withdraw

        A. retract B. accrue C. collate

_____   **9.** divide or distribute

        A. defer B. rectify C. allocate

_____   **10.** correct

        A. concur B. rectify C. capitulate

Using CONTEXT CLUES is only the first in a series of steps that you must take to improve your vocabulary. But it is an important step and involves developing a skill. This requires PRACTICE. Now it is up to you. Every time you meet an unfamiliar word, be sure to look or listen for CONTEXT CLUES. This will help you to increase your vocabulary, to build a useful word bank, and to expand your horizons.

STEP TWO: You and Featured Families

Using CONTEXT CLUES is only one method of enlarging your vocabulary. Using STRUCTURAL CLUES is a second. This simply means understanding the various parts of a word and how they are put together.

These parts consist of the ROOT WORD, the PREFIX, and the SUFFIX. Not every word, however, has all three parts.

In the word EXCHANGEABLE, CHANGE is the ROOT WORD, EX- is the PREFIX, and -ABLE is the SUFFIX.

A ROOT WORD is the main part of the word.

A PREFIX is a letter or group of letters placed at the beginning of a word to change its meaning.

A SUFFIX is a letter or group of letters placed at the end of a word. Sometimes it changes the meaning of the word. Sometimes it changes how the word is used in a sentence.

For example, the suffix ABLE changes the meaning of a root word. ABLE means *having the power or skill to do something*. Therefore, while CHANGE means *to MAKE different*, CHANGEABLE means *ABLE to make (something) different*.

On the other hand, the suffix ING changes the way a word can be used in a sentence. Consider the word CHANGING. In which of the following sentences would you use the word CHANGE? In which would you use CHANGING?

I will have to _____ the flat tire.

I am _____ the flat tire.

The meaning of both words is almost the same. Notice, however, there is a slight difference in time.

How does knowing these parts of a word help to enlarge a person's vocabulary? Seeing is believing. Try the following practice.

19

Practice One:
Adding Suffixes to a Root Word

Let's start again with the ROOT WORD CHANGE. See how many different words you can form by this method. Write the new words on the lines. The first one has been done for you.

Root Word		Suffix		New Word
1. change	**+**	-able		**1.** <u>changeable</u>
2. change	**+**	-ability		**2.** _____
3. change	**+**	-able ‚ness		**3.** _____
4. change	**+**	-ably		**4.** _____
5. change	**+**	-ful		**5.** _____
6. change	**+**	-less		**6.** _____
7. change	**+**	-ling		**7.** _____

There are seven new words. Did you know that CHANGELESS means *without change* or *constant* and CHANGELING means *a baby secretly exchanged for another?*

Now try adding both PREFIXES and SUFFIXES.

Practice Two:
Adding Prefixes and Suffixes to a Root Word

Add the PREFIX and the SUFFIX listed to the ROOT WORD. Write the new words on the lines. The first one is done for you.

Prefix	Root Word	Suffix		New Word
1. un-	change	-d		**1.** <u>unchanged</u>
2. un-	change	-able		**2.** _____
3. un-	change	-ability		**3.** _____
4. un-	change	-ing		**4.** _____

Did you remember to drop the silent E when adding the -ING above?

5. inter-	change			**5.** _____
6. inter-	change	-able		**6.** _____
7. ex-	change			**7.** _____
8. ex-	change	-ability		**8.** _____
9. ex-	change	-able		**9.** _____

Count them. You have a total of sixteen words at your command, just because you know one ROOT WORD. This is called word building.

Let's examine the idea of ROOT WORDS from another point of view. If you meet a word that you don't know, what can you learn about it from knowing the meaning of the ROOT WORD, the PREFIX, and the SUFFIX?

Consider the word UNAPPROACHABLE. If you did not know the meaning of the word, how would you use STRUCTURAL CLUES?

You would probably know that the root word APPROACH means *to go to or toward someone or something.*

From words such as UNHAPPY you would know the prefix UN- means *not.*

You also know the suffix -ABLE means *having the power or ability to do something.*

Adding these clues together, what does UNAPPROACHABLE mean in the following sentence?

Your employer is UNAPPROACHABLE. You cannot talk to him about a raise.

UNAPPROACHABLE means _____

Did you say UNAPPROACHABLE means *not able to approach someone, not able or possible to go to someone,* or *not able to talk to someone?* Any answer such as these would be correct.

That's the way STRUCTURAL CLUES help to unlock the meanings of new words. Now you have two kinds of clues to help you increase your vocabulary and unlock word meanings: CONTEXT CLUES and STRUCTURAL CLUES.

Practice Three:
Locating Root Words

Each pair of words below shares a common ROOT WORD to which a PREFIX or a SUFFIX has been added. The ROOT WORD helps you to learn the meaning of the longer words. Write the ROOT WORD on line provided. The first one is done for you.

Word Pairs

act _____

_____

_____

_____

_____

_____

1. actor—react
2. unfair—fairness
3. meatball—meaty
4. repack—package
5. directly—indirect
6. failure—unfailing

_____   **7.** dislike—likeness

_____   **8.** guilty—guiltless

_____   **9.** uncertain—certainly

_____ **10.** careful—careless

_____ **11.** return—turning

_____ **12.** shipment—reship

_____ **13.** unclear—clearly

_____ **14.** remove—movement

_____ **15.** connection—disconnect

_____ **16.** respectful—disrespect

_____ **17.** frequently—infrequent

_____ **18.** comfortable—discomfort

_____ **19.** probably—improbable

_____ **20.** location—relocate

Next let's examine prefixes. They can help you in two ways: First, they are a way to increase your vocabulary. Second, they provide clues to the meanings of unfamiliar words.

To use these clues, however, you must learn the meanings of at least the most common prefixes. Some of them you may already know.

The first group of prefixes, UN-, IN-, DIS-, and MIS-, has a negative meaning. They usually give the new word a meaning that is the opposite of the root word meaning.

Practice Four:
The Prefix UN-

Read the following sentences. Notice the CONTEXT CLUES. Underline the ROOT WORD in each CAPITALIZED word. The first one has been done for you.

1. I am UN<u>ACCUSTOMED</u> to job hunting. I have never done it before.
2. I am UNCONCERNED about the interview. I think I will do well.
3. The interviewer said I did not have enough experience. I was told I was UNQUALIFIED for the job.
4. Nobody helped me. I did the work UNASSISTED.
5. Who can do that much work in one day? I feel the request is UNREASONABLE.

What does the prefix UN- mean? Write your definition here: _____
_____

Did you remember that the prefix UN- means NOT?

Practice Five:
Definitions

Did you recognize the CONTEXT CLUES? Listed below are definitions for each CAPITALIZED word in Practice Four. Write the CAPITALIZED word that best matches each definition.

Words	*Definitions*
_____	**1.** not accustomed to or used to
_____	**2.** without help or assistance
_____	**3.** not worried or concerned
_____	**4.** lacking the necessary ability or requirements; not qualified
_____	**5.** demanding more than can be expected; not reasonable

Practice Six:
Using the Words

Write the CAPITALIZED WORD that correctly answers each of the following questions.

_____	**1.** I am not worried about my new job. Am I UNQUALIFIED or UNCONCERNED?
_____	**2.** I think that you are demanding too much of me. Do I think you are UNCONCERNED or UN-REASONABLE?
_____	**3.** I am not used to getting up so early every day. Am I UNAC-CUSTOMED to getting up early or UNCONCERNED about getting up early?

_____   **4.** Nobody helped me with the job. Was I UNCONCERNED or UNASSISTED?

_____   **5.** I need more courses for the license required by the job. At the present time am I UNASSISTED or UNQUALIFIED?

Practice Seven:
Expanding Your
Vocabulary

List five more words beginning with <u>UN-</u>, which means <u>NOT</u>. *Unhappy* is a sample. Also list the definitions. Use a dictionary to help you, if necessary.

Words	*Definitions*
1. _____	_____
2. _____	_____
3. _____	_____
4. _____	_____
5. _____	_____

Practice Eight:
The Prefix MIS-

Read the following sentences. Notice the CONTEXT CLUES. <u>Underline</u> the ROOT WORD in each CAPITALIZED word. The first one has been done for you.

1. The owner said the coach has MIS<u>MANAGED</u> the team. He claims the team was trained badly.
2. The owner also believes that the coach MISTREATED some of the players. He states that some of them did not get a fair chance to play.
3. Personally, I think that these statements will MISLEAD people. They give the wrong idea.
4. I am convinced the coach was MISJUDGED. He is a very talented person.
5. Such statements MISINFORM the public because they do not tell the whole story.

What do you think the prefix MIS- means? Write your definition here:

_____

How well did you do? The prefix MIS- means WRONG or WRONGLY.

Practice Nine:
Definitions

Did you recognize the CONTEXT CLUES? Listed below are definitions for each CAPITALIZED word in Practice Eight. Write the CAPITALIZED word that best matches each definition.

Words	*Definitions*
_____	1. give the wrong information
_____	2. made the wrong decision or judgment
_____	3. lead into the wrong thought or in the wrong direction
_____	4. handled or managed wrong
_____	5. acted wrong toward someone; treated someone wrong

Practice Ten:
Substituting Words

Read each of the following sentences. Write the word listed below that is the best substitute for the CAPITALIZED words in each sentence.

Word List: misinform, misjudge, mislead, mismanage, mistreat. Add <u>ed</u> if necessary.

_____	1. When choosing a dog, do not let a pet shop LEAD YOU IN THE WRONG DIRECTION.
_____	2. A salesperson GAVE me THE WRONG INFORMATION about how big my dog would grow.
_____	3. In addition I MADE THE WRONG DECISION about how friendly the dog would be. He just bit me.
_____	4. Someone in that pet shop must have TREATED the dog WRONG.
_____	5. I'm afraid I MANAGED BADLY the selection of my new pet.

Practice Eleven:
**Expanding Your
Vocabulary**

List five more words beginning with MIS- which mean WRONG or WRONGLY. Misconduct is a sample. Also list the definitions of these new words. Use a dictionary to help you, if necessary.

	Words	*Definitions*
1.	_____	_____
2.	_____	_____
3.	_____	_____
4.	_____	_____
5.	_____	_____

Practice Twelve:
The Prefix DIS-

Add the prefix DIS- to the following ROOT WORDS.

	Root Words	*New Words*
1.	APPEAR	_____
2.	ADVANTAGE	_____
3.	CONNECT	_____
4.	CONTENT	_____
5.	OBEY	_____

What do you think the prefix DIS- means?
   Write your definition here: _____
How well did you do? The prefix DIS- means the OPPOSITE OF or NOT.

Practice Thirteen:
Definitions

Write the word in Practice Twelve that best matches each of the following definitions. Be careful. Five are ROOT WORD definitions. Five are NEW WORD definitions.

Words	*Definitions*
_____	**1.** join
_____	**2.** drawback

_____   **3.** refuse to do something

_____   **4.** vanish

_____   **5.** something useful or helpful

_____   **6.** not satisfied

_____   **7.** break off

_____   **8.** come into sight

_____   **9.** happy, satisfied

_____   **10.** carry out orders

Practice Fourteen:
Expanding Your Vocabulary

List five more words beginning with DIS- that mean the OPPOSITE of the root word. Sample: DISAGREE. Also list the definitions of these new words. Use a dictionary, if necessary.

Words	_Definitions_
1. _____	_____
2. _____	_____
3. _____	_____
4. _____	_____
5. _____	_____

Practice Fifteen:
The Prefixes IL-, IM-, IN-, IR-

Read the following sentences. Notice the CONTEXT CLUES. Underline the ROOT WORD in each CAPITALIZED word. The first one has been done for you.

1. His behavior is IMMATURE.
2. This handwriting is ILLEGIBLE. I cannot read the writing.
3. The length of this skirt is IRREGULAR. Measure it to make it even.
4. That glass is IMPERFECT. It has a crack in it.
5. These people are INELIGIBLE for the job. They do not meet the requirements.

What do you think these prefixes IL-, IM-, IN-, and IR- mean? Write your definition here _____ .

How well did you do? These prefixes all mean NOT.

Practice Sixteen:
Definitions

Did you recognize the CONTEXT CLUES? Listed below are definitions for each CAPITALIZED word in Practice Fifteen. Write the CAPITALIZED word that best matches each definition.

Words   *Definitions*

_____   **1.** not possible to read

_____   **2.** not meeting the require-
                                        ments

_____   **3.** childish

_____   **4.** faulty

_____   **5.** uneven

Practice Seventeen:
Using the Words

Select from the word list below the word that best completes each of the following sentences.

Word List:

eligible	ineligible
legible	illegible
mature	immature
perfect	imperfect
regular	irregular

1. Stamping your feet and screaming is childish. Such behavior is

_____.

2. Unless you use a ruler the line will not be straight. It will be

_____.

3. Because you have attended all team practices you are
_____ to play in Saturday's game.

4. This diamond is _____ because it has a
large black spot in it.

5. Please make your handwriting _____.
Otherwise I will have difficulty reading your directions.

Practice Eighteen:
Expanding Your Vocabulary

List five more words beginning with IL-, IM-, IN-, or IR- that mean NOT. INCORRECT is a sample. Also list the definitions of these new words. Use a dictionary to help you, if necessary.

	Words	*Definitions*
1.	_____	_____
2.	_____	_____
3.	_____	_____
4.	_____	_____
5.	_____	_____

Practice Nineteen:
The Prefix CO-

Read the following. Notice the CONTEXT CLUES. Underline the ROOT WORD in each CAPITALIZED word. The first one has been done for you.

If we wish to CO<u>EXIST</u> and live together peacefully in this world, we must COOPERATE with each other.

Working together is the secret of success in many fields. In athletics two people may be selected as COCAPTAINS of a team. Each has a special skill that will help the team play better and hopefully win more games.

In book publishing, two people often COAUTHOR a book. One has had an exciting experience that everyone wants to read about. The other has the skills needed to write the story.

Even in the courtroom we find the need for working together. A CODEFENDANT in a murder case may find that his life depends upon someone else. Will the other person also accused of the crime tell the truth?

What do you think the prefix CO- means? Write your definitions here

_____.

How well did you do? The prefix CO- means WITH or TOGETHER.

Practice Twenty:
Definitions

Did you recognize the CONTEXT CLUES? Listed below are definitions for each CAPITALIZED word in Practice Nineteen. Write the CAPITALIZED word that best matches each definition.

Words	*Definitions*
_____	**1.** a person who works with another person on a book
_____	**2.** two people who share leadership of an athletic team
_____	**3.** a person charged with the same crime as another person
_____	**4.** to live or exist together at the same place or time
_____	**5.** to work together for a common purpose

**Practice Twenty-One:
Substituting One
Word for Many**

Write the word listed below that can be substituted in each sentence for the CAPITALIZED words.

Word List: coauthor, cocaptain, codefendant, coexist, cooperate. Add an s if necessary.

_____	**1.** These TWO PEOPLE are on trial for the theft of an automobile.
_____	**2.** The mountain climber will need a PROFESSIONAL WRITER to help him write his book.
_____	**3.** Countries will have to learn to LIVE TOGETHER if we are to have a peaceful world.
_____	**4.** One of the TWO LEADERS of the baseball team is sick.
_____	**5.** If we WORK TOGETHER, we will finish more quickly.

**Practice Twenty-Two:
The Prefix INTER-**

Read the following. Notice the CONTEXT CLUES. Underline the ROOT WORD in each CAPITALIZED word. The first one has been done for you.

1. The parts of this puzzle INTERLOCK so that it will not fall apart.
2. This is an INTERRACIAL community. People of many different races live in the area.
3. One medicine may INTERACT with another medicine and make the patient feel worse.
4. All of the problems are INTERRELATED. Living conditions, employment, education, and crime affect each other.
5. If you plan to visit Europe, you can take an INTERNATIONAL flight from Kennedy Airport.

What do you think the prefix INTER- means? Write your definition here:

_____

How well did you do? The prefix INTER- means BETWEEN or AMONG; TOGETHER.

Practice
Twenty-Three:
Definitions

Did you recognize the CONTEXT CLUES? Listed below are definitions for each CAPITALIZED word in Practice Twenty-Two. Write the CAPITALIZED word that best matches each definition.

Words	*Definitions*
_____	1. act upon or affect each other
_____	2. fit or lock together closely
_____	3. between two or more nations or countries
_____	4. between or with people of different races
_____	5. closely related or connected to each other

Practice Twenty-Four:
Using the Words

Write the word from the list below that best completes each of the following sentences.

Word List: interact, interlock, international, interracial, interrelated.

1. The man's weak heartbeat is related to other health problems. All of these problems are _____.

2. We are inviting athletes from every nation. It will be an
   _____ meet.

3. Do not add that chemical. It will _____
   with the others and cause an explosion.

4. People of all races will attend the conference. We must have an
   _____ meeting to get all points of view.

5. The parts of this gear have to _____.
   They must fit together closely so that the machine will work.

Practice Twenty-Five:
Expanding Your Vocabulary

List five more words beginning with INTER-. Also list the definitions of these new words. Use a dictionary, if necessary.

Words	*Definitions*
1. _____	_____
2. _____	_____
3. _____	_____
4. _____	_____
5. _____	_____

Practice Twenty-Six:
The Prefix PRE-

Read the following. Notice the CONTEXT CLUES. Underline the ROOT WORD in each CAPITALIZED word. The first one has been done for you.

1. We must make all of our plans before the day of the party. If we do not PREPLAN, we may forget to buy some of the food.
2. Do not decide before you know all the facts. If you PREJUDGE a person, you may make the wrong decision.
3. We must PREARRANGE the concert. If we do not make our arrangements in advance, the musicians may not be able to come.
4. A dangerous machine should have a protective guard. This PRECAUTION will prevent workers from being injured.
5. The baby was PREMATURE. The birth was not expected for two more weeks.

What do you think the prefix PRE- means? Write your definition here:

_____

How well did you do? The prefix PRE- means BEFORE.

Practice
Twenty-Seven:
Definitions

Did you recognize the CONTEXT CLUES? Listed below are definitions for each CAPITALIZED word in Practice Twenty-Six. Write the CAPITALIZED word that best matches each definition.

Words

_____

_____

_____

_____

_____

Definitions

1. arrange beforehand
2. an action taken beforehand to avoid danger; a caution or care taken beforehand
3. decide or judge beforehand; judge without knowing all the facts
4. happening before the usual time
5. plan or prepare beforehand

Practice Twenty-Eight:
Using the Words

Write the CAPITALIZED word that correctly answers each of the following questions.

_____

_____

_____

_____

1. The monthly announcement was made before the usual date. Was the announcement PREMATURE or PREARRANGED?
2. I took an umbrella with me because the weatherman had announced rain. Was I PREJUDGING or was I taking a PRECAUTION?
3. I like to prepare in advance so that I know exactly what I will need. Do I like to PREJUDGE or PREPLAN?
4. I made a mistake when I accused my friend of spreading false information. Did I PREJUDGE him or did I PREPLAN?

_____ 5. Let's set up the chairs before the meeting. Are we going to PRE-PLAN or PREARRANGE the chairs?

Practice Twenty-Nine:
Expanding Your
Vocabulary

List five more words beginning with the prefix PRE-. Also list the definitions of these new words. Use a dictionary, if necessary.

	Words	*Definitions*
1.	_____	_____
2.	_____	_____
3.	_____	_____
4.	_____	_____
5.	_____	_____

Practice Thirty:
The Prefix RE-

Read the following. Notice the CONTEXT CLUES. Underline the ROOT WORD in each CAPITALIZED word. The first one has been done for you.

1. They will have to REROUTE the airplane to Washington, D.C. Kennedy Airport in New York is closed because of the storm.
2. Save your newspapers. The town will RECYCLE the paper so that it can be used again.
3. Nobody answered the advertisement I put in the newspaper. I will have to REINSERT it for another three days.
4. Can I RESHAPE this clay? I do not like this form for a vase.
5. The mark seems to disappear and then REAPPEAR.

What do you think the prefix RE- means? Write your definition here:

_____

How well did you do? The prefix RE- means BACK or AGAIN.

Practice Thirty-One:
Definitions

Did you recognize the CONTEXT CLUES? Listed below are definitions for each CAPITALIZED word in Practice Thirty. Write the CAPITALIZED word that best matches each definition.

Words	*Definitions*
_____	1. come into view again; appear again
_____	2. treat or process something so that it can be used again
_____	3. set in place again; insert again
_____	4. send again by a different course or road; route again in a different way
_____	5. form or mold again; shape again

**Practice Thirty-Two:
Using the Words**

Write the word from the list below that best completes each of the following sentences.

Word List: reappear, recycle, reinsert, reroute, reshape.

1. I have been wearing my hair shaped like this for two years. Can you _____ it for me? I would like a different hair style.

2. The ghost appears each month at full moon. Tonight the moon will be full. Do you think the ghost will _____?

3. In my home we give clothes that we have outgrown to another member of the family. We jokingly say that we _____ clothes.

4. The bridge has been destroyed by the flood. The police will have to _____ the traffic.

5. This piece dropped out of the puzzle. Can you _____ it?

**Practice Thirty-Three:
Expanding Your
Vocabulary**

List five more words beginning with the prefix RE-. Also list the definitions of these new words. Use a dictionary, if necessary.

	Words		*Definitions*
1.	_____		_____
2.	_____		_____
3.	_____		_____
4.	_____		_____
5.	_____		_____

Practice Thirty-Four:
The Prefix <u>SEMI-</u>

Read the following. Notice the CONTEXT CLUES. <u>Underline</u> the ROOT WORD in each CAPITALIZED word. The first one has been done for you.

1. That person is a SEMI-<u>INVALID.</u> He was injured in an automobile accident and can no longer walk very far.
2. This apartment is only a SEMIPERMANENT arrangement. I will be moving to a new apartment next month.
3. In order to play in the final rounds of the game, you must be one of the winners in the SEMIFINAL contest.
4. The patient is not unconscious, nor is he fully awake. He is SEMICONSCIOUS.
5. Does this company pay its employees once a month or SEMIMONTHLY?

Did you notice that the word <u>SEMI-INVALID</u> has a dash, a hyphen, between the two parts of the word? That is because the prefix ends with an <u>i</u> and the root word begins with the same letter. This rule applies only to double vowels.

Now what do you think the prefix SEMI- means? Write your definition here: _____

How well did you do? The prefix SEMI- means HALF or NOT COMPLETELY.

Practice Thirty-Five:
Definitions

Did you recognize the CONTEXT CLUES? Listed below are definitions for each CAPITALIZED word in Practice Thirty-Four. Write the CAPITALIZED word that best matches each definition.

Words		*Definitions*
_____	1.	half or partly awake or conscious
_____	2.	immediately before the final match in a tournament
_____	3.	partly disabled by injury or disease
_____	4.	happening twice a month
_____	5.	not completely permanent; lasting only for a limited time

Practice Thirty-Six:
Using the Words

Write the word listed below that best completes each of the following sentences.

Word List: semiconscious, semifinal, semi-invalid, semimonthly, semi-permanent.

1. This plastic splint is only _____. The doctor will replace it with a permanent cast.
2. Until my broken leg has healed, I will be a _____.
3. The nurse told me the doctor wished to see me twice a month. She will make a _____ appointment for me.
4. The football player was hit so hard that he was only _____. He had to be helped from the field by the team doctor.
5. She was the winner of the _____ contest, but lost the final contest.

Practice Thirty-Seven:
Expanding Your Vocabulary

List five more words beginning with the prefix SEMI-. Also list the definitions of these new words. Use a dictionary, if necessary.

Words	*Definitions*
1. _____	_____

2. _____   _____
3. _____   _____
4. _____   _____
5. _____   _____

**Practice Thirty-Eight:
The Prefix SUB-**

Read the following. Notice the CONTEXT CLUES. Underline the ROOT WORD in each CAPITALIZED word. The first one has been done for you.

1. This apartment is very cold. As a result the old man's temperature is SUBNORMAL.
2. We can SUBDIVIDE this apartment into two smaller apartments.
3. We can take the SUBWAY to Times Square.
4. The SUBCOMMITTEE will report to the main committee within two weeks.
5. An apartment without heat or running water is SUBSTANDARD.

Now what do you think the prefix SUB- means? Write your definition here: _____

How well did you do? The prefix SUB- means UNDER, BELOW, LOWER IN RANK.

**Practice Thirty-Nine:
Definitions**

Did you recognize the CONTEXT CLUES? Listed below are definitions for each CAPITALIZED word in Practice Thirty-Eight. Write the CAPITALIZED word that best matches each definition.

Words	*Definitions*
_____	1. a committee acting under a main committee
_____	2. divide or separate after the first division
_____	3. below the normal or average
_____	4. below the usual standard or quality
_____	5. a railroad under the ground

Practice Forty:
Using the Words

Write the word from the list below that best answers each of the following questions.

Word List: subcommittee, subdivide, subnormal, substandard, subway.

_____   1. We took an underground railroad to Madison Square Garden. What did we take?

_____   2. The towels that were on sale were marked <u>irregular</u> and <u>seconds.</u> They were below the manufacturer's standards. What were they?

_____   3. We planned to make the room into two smaller rooms. What were we going to do to the room?

_____   4. The committee selected a group of its members to get the information needed. What did they form?

_____   5. The child's temperature was below normal. What was his temperature?

Practice Forty-One:
Expanding Your Vocabulary

List five more words beginning with the prefix SUB-. Also list the definitions of these new words. Use a dictionary, if necessary.

Words	*Definitions*
1. _____	_____
2. _____	_____
3. _____	_____
4. _____	_____
5. _____	_____

Practice Forty-Two:
The Prefix SUPER-

Read the following. Notice the CONTEXT CLUES. Underline the ROOT WORD in each CAPITALIZED word. The first one has been done for you.

1. America, Russia, China, and other nations are SUPER<u>POWERS</u>. They influence world affairs.
2. Superman is SUPERHUMAN. He does things that the normal person cannot do.
3. The weeds are SUPERABUNDANT. There are so many they are killing the rose bushes.
4. Ghosts are SUPERNATURAL.
5. Some people are SUPERSENSITIVE. They are hurt if everyone doesn't agree with their ideas.

What do you think the prefix SUPER- means? Write your definitions here:

_____

How well did you do? The prefix SUPER- means OVER, ABOVE, MORE THAN.

Practice Forty-Three:
Definitions

Did you recognize the CONTEXT CLUES? Listed below are definitions for each CAPITALIZED word in Practice Forty-Two. Write the CAPITALIZED word that best matches each definition.

Words	*Definitions*
_____	1. more than is necessary; very abundant
_____	2. more easily hurt than the average person
_____	3. more than human strength or power
_____	4. over or above the natural; not found in this natural world
_____	5. a nation having more power than other nations; a country that influences world affairs; usually a country that has nuclear weapons

Practice Forty-Four:
Using the Words

Write the word from the list below that best completes each of the following sentences.

Word List: superabundant, superhuman, supernatural, superpower, supersensitive.

1. A person that is hurt very quickly and easily is _____

_____ .

2. A ghost is not natural. It is _____ .

3. A world power with nuclear weapons such as the United States is called a

_____ .

4. If you can lift a car, you have more than human strength. You have

_____ strength.

5. Weeds are always abundant. This year, however, there are more than

ever. They are _____ .

Practice Forty-Five:
Expanding Your Vocabulary

List five more words beginning with the prefix SUPER- . Also list the definitions of these new words. Use a dictionary, if necessary.

Words	*Definitions*
1. _____	_____
2. _____	_____
3. _____	_____
4. _____	_____
5. _____	_____

Practice Forty-Six:
The Prefix TRANS-

Read the following. Notice the CONTEXT CLUES. Underline the ROOT WORD in each CAPITALIZED word. The first one has been done for you.

1. We took a TRANSATLANTIC flight from New York to London.
2. The liquid that man is drinking will TRANSFORM him into a wolf.
3. A business TRANSACTION such as selling a house can bring a profit to the seller.

4. A kidney TRANSPLANT means moving a kidney from one person to another.

5. We plan to take a TRANSCONTINENTAL flight from New York City to California.

What do you think the prefix TRANS- means? Write your definition here:
_____ .

How well did you do? The prefix TRANS- means ACROSS, THROUGH or to CHANGE.

Practice Forty-Seven:
Definitions

Did you recognize the CONTEXT CLUES? Listed below are definitions for each CAPITALIZED word in Practice Forty-Six. Write the CAPITAL-IZED word that best matches each definition.

Words	*Definitions*
_____	1. a business deal; a business action that has been carried through and completed
_____	2. across a continent
_____	3. across the Atlantic Ocean
_____	4. change from one form to another
_____	5. move from one place to another

Practice Forty-Eight:
Using the Words

Write the word from the list below that best completes each of the following sentences.

Word List: transaction, transcontinental, transatlantic, transform, transplant.

1. I want to move these plants to another place in the garden. I plan to _____ them tomorrow.

2. That business _____ was very successful. I made a thousand dollars.

3. If you live in eastern United States and want to fly to the west coast, you will take a _____ flight.

4. What does it take to _____ a liquid into a gas?

5. If you are going across the Atlantic Ocean you will have to take a _____ flight.

Practice Forty-Nine:
Expanding Your Vocabulary

List five more words beginning with the prefix TRANS-. Also list the definitions of these new words. Use a dictionary, if necessary.

	Words	*Definitions*
1.	_____	_____
2.	_____	_____
3.	_____	_____
4.	_____	_____
5.	_____	_____

You have worked now with ROOT WORDS and PREFIXES. There is one final WORD part—the SUFFIX. This is a letter or group of letters FIXED or placed at the END OF THE ROOT WORD. Let's identify some of these SUFFIXES.

Practice Fifty:
Locating Suffixes

Each pair of words below shares a common SUFFIX. This is a group of letters added to the end of both words. Write these SUFFIXES on the lines provided. The first one is done for you.

	Word Pairs	*Suffixes*
1.	agreeable—acceptable	-able _____
2.	personal—regional	_____
3.	considerate—liquidate	_____
4.	crooked—featured	_____
5.	adviser—boiler	_____
6.	careful—wishful	_____
7.	childhood—falsehood	_____
8.	terrify—magnify	_____

9. atomic—democratic _____

10. cooking—eating _____

11. selfish—childish _____

12. alarmist—novelist _____

13. ability—sanity _____

14. collective—creative _____

15. terrorize—centralize _____

16. noiseless—meatless _____

17. softly—slowly _____

18. shipment—agreement _____

19. sweetness—bitterness _____

20. actor—conductor _____

21. dangerous—famous _____

22. friendship—championship _____

23. gangster—youngster _____

24. afterward—northward _____

25. fishy—salty _____

Practice Fifty-One:
Adding Suffixes

Now you try your hand at making new words. To each ROOT WORD add the suffix listed. Write the new word on the line provided.

Root Word		Suffix		New Word
1. comfort	+	-able	=	_____
2. accident	+	-al	=	_____
3. accept	+	-ance	=	_____
4. deport	+	-ation	=	_____
5. hunt	+	-ed	=	_____
6. start	+	-er	=	_____
7. sorrow	+	-ful	=	_____
8. fish	+	-ing	=	_____
9. hero	+	-ism	=	_____
10. humor	+	-ist	=	_____
11. collect	+	-ive	=	_____
12. central	+	-ize	=	_____

13. fear	**+**	-less	**=**	_____
14. exact	**+**	-ly	**=**	_____
15. lone	**+**	-ly	**=**	_____
16. achieve	**+**	-ment	**=**	_____
17. deaf	**+**	-ness	**=**	_____
18. prosper	**+**	-ous	**=**	_____
19. trouble	**+**	-some	**=**	_____
20. storm	**+**	-y	**=**	_____

Practice Fifty-Two:
Using Context Clues to Help Select the Correct Form of a Word

Above each group of sentences are three CAPITALIZED words. In the space provided write the CAPITALIZED word that best completes each sentence.

1. AMBITION, AMBITIOUS, AMBITIOUSLY
   A. He worked _____ to reach his goal.
   B. He wants the job because he is a very _____ person.
   C. His _____ is to become a lawyer.

2. ASSIST, ASSISTANCE, ASSISTANT
   A. The magician's _____ disappeared in a puff of smoke.
   B. The magician needs the _____ of two people to put the chains around the magic box.
   C. The magician asked for someone from the audience to _____ with the trick.

3. COMMUNICATE, COMMUNICATION, COMMUNICABLE
   A. Measles and mumps are _____ diseases. A healthy person can get these diseases from someone who is ill.
   B. We _____ with each other by talking.
   C. TV and radio are two forms of _____ .

4. CONFIDE, CONFIDENCE, CONFIDENT

    A. I have no doubts. I am _____ that you will succeed.

    B. I will be glad to listen to your problem. Will you _____ _____ in me?

    C. I have _____ in your ability to do the job.

5. DEMONSTRATE, DEMONSTRATION, DEMONSTRATIVE

    A. Will you _____ how to use this new pump?

    B. She is a very _____ person. You can tell how she feels by the way that she acts.

    C. The _____ was helpful. It convinced the mayor that many people are opposed to the new tax.

6. ENDURE, ENDURANCE, ENDURABLE

    A. This boxer has tremendous _____. He never seems to tire.

    B. How can the fighter _____ so many body punches?

    C. Perhaps the punishment is _____ because he knows it is the last round of the bout.

7. RECUR, RECURRENCE, RECURRENT

    A. This is a _____ of the same problem that I had with my car a month ago.

    B. Why can't some mechanic fix this _____ problem?

    C. When can I expect it to _____?

8. RESIST, RESISTANCE, RESISTANT

    A. My _____ is low because I have been sick.

    B. This material is wrinkle _____.

    C. Who can _____ a delicious dessert?

9. SKILL, SKILLFUL, SKILLFULLY

    A. Her greatest _____ is her ability to locate mechanical problems.

    B. She also works _____ with tools.

    C. She is a very _____ human being.

10. STYLE, STYLISH, STYLISHLY

    A. Do you like to dress _____?

    B. What is the latest _____ in men's clothing?

    C. Do you think that suit is _____?

Practice Fifty-Three:
Definitions

Write the word that best matches each definition.

	Definitions	Words
_____	1. make known or share	a. ambition
_____	2. show	b. assist
_____	3. happen again	c. communicate
_____	4. ability	d. confide
_____	5. help	e. demonstrate
_____	6. fashion in clothing	f. endure
_____	7. oppose	g. recur
_____	8. desire to succeed	h. resist
_____	9. put up with or stand	i. skill
_____	10. tell as a secret	j. style

Practice Fifty-Four:
Adding Suffixes

Change or add a suffix so that each CAPITALIZED word fits the context. Then write the new word in the space provided.

1. AMBITION   He is a very _____ person.

2. ASSIST   I need your _____.

3. COMMUNICATE   The common cold is a _____ disease.

4. CONFIDE   I have _____ in your ability.

5. DEMONSTRATE   This _____ will teach you how to operate the new equipment.

6. ENDURE   His _____ is low because he is not in good physical condition.

7. RECUR   The _____ of the problem made me seek professional help.

8. RESIST   There is great _____ to higher taxes.

9. SKILL   He handled the problem _____.

10. STYLE   Do you like _____ clothing?

Practice Fifty-Five:
Funny Foods

What is being said in each of the sentences below? Try rewriting each sentence using standard English for the CAPITALIZED expression. If necessary, use a dictionary.

1. Do you have enough LETTUCE to go to the movies?

_____

2. That's SOUR GRAPES.

_____

3. The play is a TURKEY.

_____

4. That problem is a HOT POTATO.

_____

5. Your car is a LEMON.

_____

6. He's AS COOL AS A CUCUMBER.

_____

7. Don't get involved in that RHUBARB.

_____

8. You're NUTS!

_____

9. How much DOUGH do you have?

_____

10. You're being very PIGHEADED.

_____

Practice Fifty-Six:
Some Teasers

Where do you find an EAR? Write a word ending in EAR that fulfills each description. The first one is done for you.

year _____   **1.** twelve months

_____   **2.** when you cry

_____   **3.** when you begin a letter

_____   **4.** when you are frightened

_____   **5.** when you listen

_____   **6.** when you are close

_____   **7.** when you are on a ten-speed bicycle

_____   **8.** when you are at the end of a line

Practice Fifty-Seven:
Words from Words

What is <u>LINGUISTIC</u> <u>OBFUSCATION</u>? Stated in simple terms LINGUISTIC OBFUSCATION is language confusion. It is a phrase used to criticize those who use large words and complicated sentences to impress people. How many small words can you make from the phrase LINGUISTIC OBFUSCATION?

_____   _____

_____   _____

_____   _____

_____   _____

You and Compound Companions

One way of describing something new is to combine two words to form a new word. This combination gives the new word a special meaning different from the original meanings of the separate words. For example, a headline is not a line on one's head, nor is shorthand a small hand.

In addition, compounds may be written in three different ways. The words may be combined into a single word such as *crossroad*. They may be hyphenated such as *cross-examine*, or they may be written as two separate words such as *cross fire*.

Finally, more than two words may be combined. For example, we have such compounds as *one-on-one*, *pay-as-you-go*, *time and a half* and many others.

Practice One:
The Challenge

Below are two word lists. Take a word from LIST A and combine it with a word from LIST B to make a compound word. Use each word only once even though it may fit with several words. The first one is done for you. For help, use a dictionary.

Word List A	Word List B	Compound Words
air	back	1. airport
any	book	2. _____
care	boy	3. _____
cross	cap	4. _____
fire	come	5. _____
knee	house	6. _____
land	less	7. _____
life	line	8. _____
mean	load	9. _____
mid	lord	10. _____

over	man	11. _____
pocket	night	12. _____
pay	out	13. _____
play	port	14. _____
quarter	road	15. _____
sales	roll	16. _____
side	table	17. _____
time	thing	18. _____
truck	walk	19. _____
through	while	20. _____

Practice Two:
Hidden Compounds

Here is your chance to be a detective again. Each of the following sentences suggests a compound word. Write the compound word. Use a dictionary, if necessary. The first one is done for you.

seaside _____

_____

_____

_____

_____

_____

_____

_____

_____

_____

_____

_____

_____

1. He lives by the side of the sea.
2. We need a man in the show.
3. Is it under your foot?
4. Keep your eye on the ball.
5. That man is super.
6. Will the horse work?
7. I need a piece for the center.
8. This one has less weight.
9. Is the cat wild?
10. He hurt the bone in his back.
11. The ambassador is a man of state.
12. Don't hit that runner in the road.
13. We must find a place for a fire.
14. What is the word to watch for?
15. Can you see any mark on the land?

_____   16. There is a bug in the bed.

_____   17. Are they struck by the moon?

_____   18. Is this the track that goes back?

_____   19. It tells a tale.

_____   20. A yard of vines is pretty.

Practice Three:
Recognizing a Misfit

Write the compound word that does NOT belong in the series. The first one is done for you. Notice that WINDOW is one half of each compound in Series 1. As a result, STORMBOUND is a misfit.

stormbound_____   1. windowpane, windowsill, stormwindow, stormbound

_____   2. withdraw, drawback, backboard, drawbridge

_____   3. horseshoe, overshoe, shoetree, treetop

_____   4. whenever, however, evergreen, greenhouse

_____   5. closeout, outlet, blackbird, blackout

_____   6. tugboat, rowboat, workhouse, boathouse

_____   7. stickball, nightstick, stickpin, pinup

_____   8. swordfish, fishtail, tailspin, bluefish

_____   9. sidelight, outside, inside, income

_____   10. paycheck, checkout, salesclerk, salescheck

_____   11. borderline, sideline, borderland, lineup

_____   12. fingernail, nailfile, nailhead, headline

_____   13. speedway, raceway, racetrack, wayside

_____   14. slipsheet, slipover, slipcover, coverall

_____   15. bowknot, bowleg, rainbow, raincoat

_____   16. homework, workout, homeroom, workroom

_____   17. mankind, marksman, sportsman, sportscar

_____   18. birthday, daylight, nighttime, daytime

_____   19. kickoff, offside, playback, playoff

_____   20. turntable, tabletop, cardtable, cardplayer

Practice Four:
Interesting Pairs—UP and DOWN

The following pairs of compounds express opposite or nearly opposite ideas. Can you match each pair on the word list with the correct definition below? Use a dictionary, if necessary.

Word List:

upbeat	downbeat
upstate	downstate
upstream	downstream
uptown	downtown
upwind	downwind

Words   *Definitions*

_____   **1.** against the flow of the stream

_____   **2.** with the flow of the stream

_____   **3.** in the business district

_____   **4.** away from the business area

_____   **5.** an accented beat in music

_____   **6.** an unaccented beat in music

_____   **7.** against the wind

_____   **8.** with the wind

_____   **9.** southern part of a state

_____   **10.** northern part of a state

Practice Five:
Using the Words

Use one of the UP or DOWN words in Practice Four to complete each of the following sentences.

1. I am trout fishing _____ with the current.

2. I work _____ in the business district.

3. In touring the state we will go _____ to visit the places of interest in the north.

4. This song starts on an unaccented note. Watch for the _____.

5. On a boat, be sure to throw the water _____. Otherwise, you will get it back in your face.

Practice Six:
**Interesting
Pairs—More UP
and DOWN**

Match each pair on the word list with the correct definition below. Use a dictionary, if necessary.

Word List:

downgrade	upgrade
downstage	upstage
downhill	uphill
downswing	upswing
downward	upward

Words | *Definitions*

_____

_____

_____

_____

_____

_____

_____

_____

_____

_____

1. a downward swing also, less business activity
2. an upward swing; also, more business activity
3. to improve the quality or grade of something
4. to lower the price or grade of something
5. moving from lower to higher
6. moving from higher to lower
7. front of stage; near audience
8. back of stage
9. going down a hill; also easy
10. going up a hill; also difficult

Practice Seven:
Using the Words

Use one of the UP or DOWN words in Practice Six to complete each of the following sentences.

1. Now that we've passed the difficult part, the rest of the way will be all

   _____.

2. During a good period, business activity is on the _____.

3. The stockmarket was falling. This _____ movement discouraged buyers.

4. Move _____ so that you will be closer to
   the audience.
5. We will have to _____ the quality of this
   product if we want people to buy it.

Practice Eight:
**Interesting
Pairs—OVER and
UNDER**

Match each pair on the word list with the correct definition below.

Word List:

overbid	underbid
overcharge	undercharge
overdone	underdone
overrate	underrate
overpass	underpass

Words

_____
_____
_____

_____

_____

_____

_____
_____
_____

_____

Definitions

1. not completely cooked
2. cooked too long
3. bid or offer more than something is worth
4. bid less or offer to do something
   for less
5. lower level of two highways
   that cross
6. upper level of two highways
   that cross
7. charge too much for something
8. charge too little for something
9. rate or estimate the value of
   something too low
10. rate or estimate the value of
    something too high

Practice Nine:
Using the Words

Use one of the HIGH or LOW words in Practice Eight to complete each of the following sentences:

1. Do not _____ the other team. They have a lot of talent.

2. I was charged too much and received a $2.00 refund. That was the exact amount of the _____.

3. The meat was _____. It was almost raw, and no one could eat it.

4. There was an _____ so that cars could go under the highway.

5. The company _____ on the job. As a result the work was given to the company with the lower bid.

Practice Ten:
Interesting Pairs—HIGH and LOW

Match each pair on the word list with the correct definition below. Use a dictionary, if necessary.

Word List:

high-grade	low-grade
highland	lowland
high-level	low-level
high-pressure	low-pressure
high-spirited	low-spirited

Words

_____

_____

_____

_____

_____

Definitions

1. including strain and pressure; also using forceful sales method

2. easygoing; not forceful; little pressure

3. sad, little spirit

4. lively, bold, daring, spirited

5. high, superior quality

6. low, inferior quality

_____ 7. very important; of high importance or position

_____ 8. unimportant; of low importance or position

_____ 9. mountainous land

_____ 10. land that is lower than the surrounding land

Practice Eleven:
Using the Words

Use one of the HIGH or LOW words in Practice Ten to complete each of the following sentences.

1. It is cooler in the _____ than it is in the valley.

2. The _____ leather split before the shoes were a month old.

3. In a race I like a _____ horse.

4. The salesman used a _____ sales pitch. He did not try to pressure me into buying.

5. A _____ meeting is planned with all the heads of state attending.

Practice Twelve:
Compound
Collectibles

Certain words in our language are used much more frequently than others to form compounds. Use your dictionary to see how many compound words you can discover beginning with each of the CAPITALIZED words below. List the compound words on a separate sheet of paper. Your list will be a long one. Each of the words below has many more than ten compound forms.

BACK   CROSS   OPEN   SELF   SHORT

Practice Thirteen:
Colorful
Compounds

There are many compound words that have a color as one part of the compound. Use your dictionary to define each of the CAPITALIZED words below. Then list a second example of a colorful compound. Also define the second example. The first two are done for you.

Definitions	Colorful Compound List
a sale of sheets, towels, etc. _____	1. WHITE SALE
top of a wave _____	2. WHITECAP
_____	3. YELLOW PAGES
_____	4. _____
_____	5. PINK EYE
_____	6. _____
_____	7. PURPLE HEART
_____	8. _____
_____	9. ORANGE PEKOE
_____	10. _____
_____	11. BLUE CHIP
_____	12. _____
_____	13. BLACK MARKET
_____	14. _____
_____	15. RED ALERT
_____	16. _____
_____	17. GREENBACK
_____	18. _____
_____	19. BROWNOUT
_____	20. _____

STEP FOUR: You and Helpful Histories

Words, like people, have a past and a present, and many have a future. Like people, some are more interesting and more exciting than others. Like people, words move from country to country, adjusting to the needs of the times and changing their appearances. At one time certain words are socially acceptable and at another time socially unacceptable. In order to survive, some "roll with the punches." Others, however, just die.

Words are like good friends. They become more interesting as we learn more about them.

Here are some words with interesting pasts. These words come to us from classical mythology and history.

Self-Test A: How many of the CAPITALIZED words do you know? Next to each number write the letter of the best definition.

Words   *Definitions*

_____ **1.** MESMERIZE   A. criticize B. hypnotize C. scandalize

_____ **2.** GERRYMANDER   A. divide into election districts B. represent a group C. campaign for election

_____ **3.** MENTOR   A. child B. plumber C. teacher

_____ **4.** NEMESIS   A. punisher B. wanderer C. conductor

_____ **5.** TANTALIZE   A. satisfy B. fulfill C. tease

_____ **6.** TITANIC   A. weak B. gigantic C. little

59

_____ **7.** CHAUVINISM   A. superpatriotism   B. fascism   C. communism

_____ **8.** BOYCOTT   A. group support   B. refusal to buy or trade with   C. group acceptance

_____ **9.** SADISTIC   A. getting pleasure from one's good deeds   B. getting pleasure from giving pain to others   C. getting pleasure from one's own pain

_____ **10.** MASOCHISTIC   A. getting pleasure from giving pain to others   B. getting pleasure from one's own pain   C. getting pleasure from one's good deeds

Read the following short histories of the CAPITALIZED words.

TANTALIZE

King Tantalus displeased the Greek gods. He was punished by being put into water up to his chin. Delicious fruit hung from a tree over his head. When he tried to drink the water or reach for the fruit, they were pulled from his reach. Today TANTALIZE means tease.

TITANIC

The Titans were the early giant gods of the Greeks. They protected the heavens against enemies. Today TITANIC means very large, gigantic.

MENTOR

Mentor was a friend of the Greek hero Odysseus. He had the job of educating Odysseus's son Telemachus. Today MENTOR means trusted teacher or guide.

NEMESIS

Nemesis was the Greek goddess of fate. She punished people who had too much pride. Today NEMESIS means punishment or punisher; source of ruin or downfall.

BOYCOTT

Captain Charles Boycott refused to lower the Irish tenants' rents. As a result they would have nothing to do with him. Today BOYCOTT means to refuse to do business with, or associate with another person, business, or country.

CHAUVINISM

Nicolas Chauvin was a soldier who admired Napoleon greatly. He was so patriotic he was made fun of in cartoons. Today CHAUVINISM means superpatriotism and also boastful enthusiasm for one's own sex or group.

GERRYMANDER

In 1812 Governor Elbridge Gerry and his party changed the boundaries of the voting districts in Massachusetts. These changes gave their party more political power. One district looked like a salamander, an animal shaped like a lizard. Therefore, a newspaper editor invented the word GERRYMANDER from Gerry's name and the last half of salamander. Today changing boundaries for political advantage is called gerrymandering.

MESMERIZE

Mesmerize comes from the name of the Austrian doctor, Freidrich Anton Mesmer, who demonstrated hypnotism in 1775. Today MESMERIZE means to hypnotize, spellbind, bewitch, and fascinate.

MASOCHISTIC

Masochistic comes from the name of Leopold von Sacher-Masoch, an Austrian writer. He described the abnormal situation of getting pleasure from one's own pain or embarrassment. Today MASOCHISTIC means getting pleasure from one's own pain.

SADISTIC

The Marquis de Sade, 1740–1814, described getting pleasure from physically or mentally hurting others. Today anyone who is deliberately cruel or brutal is called SADISTIC.

Practice One: Definitions

Listed below are definitions for each CAPITALIZED word in the stories above. Write the CAPITALIZED word that best matches each definition. After each definition there is a clue to help you match words and meanings.

_____   **1.** tease; torment; taunt; lead on
(ta-)

_____   2. huge; gigantic; of great size,
                                      strength or power (ti-)

_____   3. teacher; guide; instructor
                                      (men-)

_____   4. punishment; punisher; source
                                      of ruin or downfall (n-)

_____   5. cruel and brutal (s-)

_____   6. hypnotize; bewitch; spellbound
                                      (mes-)

_____   7. getting pleasure from one's own
                                      pain (mas-)

_____   8. divide voting districts for unfair
                                      political advantage (ge-)

_____   9. superpatriotism; exaggerated
                                      attachment to a cause (ch-)

_____   10. refusal to do business with or as-
                                      sociate with (b-)

Practice Two:
Matching

Write the word that best matches each definition. The following definitions may be slightly different from the original definitions.

	Definitions	_Words_
_____	1. guide; teacher	**A.** nemesis
_____	2. tease; tempt; lead on	**B.** titanic
_____	3. punisher or punishment	**C.** tantalize
_____	4. gigantic	**D.** mentor
_____	5. superpatriotism	**E.** gerrymander
_____	6. refusal to deal with	**F.** mesmerize
_____	7. hypnotize; spellbind	**G.** masochistic
_____	8. cruel, brutal	**H.** chauvinism
_____	9. getting pleasure from one's own pain	**I.** boycott
_____	10. divide districts for political advantage	**J.** sadistic

Practice Three:
Using the Words

Now, can you use the vocabulary words? Answer each question either YES or NO.

1. Would you call a hurricane a TITANIC storm? _____

2. Would a school be a place to find a MENTOR? _____

3. Would you be glad to see your NEMESIS? _____

4. When you are dieting, are you likely to be TANTA-LIZED by an ice cream soda? _____

5. Could you BOYCOTT a store that charged too much for jeans? _____

6. Would a SADISTIC person be a kindly doctor? _____

7. Do you think a MASOCHISTIC person is a happy person? _____

8. Do politicians sometimes GERRYMANDER districts to be sure they win elections? _____

9. Is it possible for a hypnotist to MESMERIZE a person? _____

10. Would a person be guilty of CHAUVINISM if that person refused to salute the flag of his country? _____

Practice Four:
Word Families

Our vocabulary can be expanded by adding or subtracting word endings. Here are some new entries for your word bank. The following abbreviations are used: v. (verb), n. (noun), and adj. (adjective).

1. TANTALIZE-v.
   TANTALIZER-n.   one who teases; taunts
2. TITANIC-adj.
   TITAN-n.   one of gigantic size, power or achievement
3. SADISTIC-adj.
   SADISM-n.   excessive cruelty
4. MESMERIZE-v.
   MESMERISM-n.   hypnotism
5. MASOCHISTIC-adj.
   MASOCHISM-n.   getting pleasure from being hurt

Can you use these new words? Write the word needed to complete each of the following sentences.

1. Because of his enormous strength he was known as a _____

_____ .

2. The use of _____ was a cruel way prison guards kept discipline.

3. The hypnotist uses _____ in his TV act.

4. He was known as the neighborhood _____ because he teased the children.

5. _____ is a mental sickness because the person involved intentionally hurts himself.

Practice Five:
Review

How many of these CAPITALIZED words have you learned? Next to each number write the letter of the best definition.

_____ 1. TANTALIZE   A. gratify   B. tease   C. satisfy

_____ 2. GERRYMANDER   A. represent a district   B. divide election districts   C. campaign in a district

_____ 3. BOYCOTT   A. support   B. accept   C. avoid

_____ 4. MENTOR   A. adviser   B. student   C. sailor

_____ 5. TITANIC   A. huge   B. small   C. weak

_____ 6. CHAUVINISM   A. fascism   B. communism   C. superpatriotism

_____ 7. SADISTIC   A. getting pleasure from one's own pain   B. getting pleasure from giving pain to others   C. getting sad from pain

_____ 8. NEMESIS   A. wanderer   B. punisher   C. comic

_____ 9. MESMERIZE   A. hypnotize   B. criticize   C. scandalize

_____ 10. MASOCHISTIC   A. getting pleasure from one's own pain   B. getting mad from pain   C. getting pleasure from giving pain to others

Very often we use words and expressions whose origins are unknown to us. These expressions, once understood, add color to our language.

Self-Test B: How many of the CAPITALIZED words or expressions do you know? Next to the number write the letter of the best definition.

Words	*Definitions*
_____ 1. ACHILLES' HEEL	A. magic waters B. a weak spot C. a small heel
_____ 2. LIKE A DUTCH UNCLE	A. kind advice B. severe disapproval C. a Dutch habit
_____ 3. BAKER'S DOZEN	A. twelve of anything B. a dozen plus one C. one less than a dozen
_____ 4. FIASCO	A. failure B. success C. Italian
_____ 5. MIDAS TOUCH	A. unsuccessful in earning money B. power of a king C. successful in earning money
_____ 6. LETHARGY	A. vigor B. laziness C. liveliness
_____ 7. LABYRINTH	A. maze B. command C. laboratory
_____ 8. SWORD OF DAMOCLES	A. a sword with magic powers B. threat of danger C. a sword of Syracuse
_____ 9. ATLAS	A. book of maps B. image C. mapmaker
_____ 10. INVESTIGATE	A. guess B. ignore C. track

AN ACHILLES' HEEL

Achilles was a Greek hero. As a baby, his mother dipped him in the magic waters of the river Styx. As a result he could not be injured anywhere except in his heel. This was his only weak spot. Therefore, any weak point is known as an ACHILLES' HEEL

ATLAS

The name ATLAS brings to mind two pictures: a man who bears a heavy burden and a book of maps. ATLAS was a powerful Greek giant who was forced to support the heavens with his head and hands. Mapmakers began using pictures of ATLAS supporting the weight of the world. Today, an ATLAS is a book of maps.

BAKER'S DOZEN

A dozen plus one! This practice goes back to the thirteenth century when a merchant caught giving a customer short weight was severely punished. Therefore, the baker gave his customer an extra loaf of bread to avoid the possibility of such a punishment.

LIKE A DUTCH UNCLE

In the past the English made fun of many Dutch customs. A Dutch bargain was a one-sided bargain, Dutch nightingales were frogs, and a Dutch treat was a meal for which each person paid his own bill. A DUTCH UNCLE was pictured as a mean, strict, demanding individual. The expression LIKE A DUTCH UNCLE now means severe criticism or disapproval.

FIASCO

The Italian word FIASCO originally meant bottle or flask. In Venice, glass that was not perfect was made into a flask. No glass blower was happy when he failed and had to make a fiasco, or flask. Today FIASCO means a complete failure.

INVESTIGATE

Today detectives look for fingerprints when they are searching for a criminal. When a convict in ancient Rome broke away from his guards, he was caught by following his tracks or footprints. The English word INVESTIGATE—to look into, to study, to probe—comes from the Latin verb *investigare,* meaning to track.

LABYRINTH

King Minos of Crete needed a prison for the Minotaur, a monster half-bull and half-man. Therefore, he had Daedalus, a skilled worker, build a series of twisting confusing passageways, which kept the monster trapped. Today a LABYRINTH is a series of winding passages or paths in which it is easy to lose one's way; it is a maze.

LETHARGY

The River Lethe in Greek mythology flowed through Hades, the underground world. Anyone who drank its water forgot the past. LETHARGY now means lack of energy, laziness, sluggishness, drowsiness.

MIDAS TOUCH

The Greek king Midas was given the power to turn whatever he touched into gold. The MIDAS TOUCH is now used to describe a person who is very successful earning money.

SWORD OF DAMOCLES

A ruler of ancient Syracuse invited Damocles to a dinner party. Damocles enjoyed the party until he looked up and noticed a sword hanging over his head by a single hair. The ruler had done this to show Damocles that holding an important position or job also could mean danger and unhappiness. Today we refer to the SWORD OF DAMOCLES as a threat of danger.

Practice Six:
Definitions

Listed below are definitions for each CAPITALIZED word in the stories above. Write the capitalized word that best matches each definition. After each definition there is a clue.

_____

_____

_____

_____

_____

_____

_____

_____

_____

_____

1. maze; place full of passageways (l-)

2. track; explore; examine closely (in-)

3. book of maps (a-)

4. weak spot; (A- h-)

5. severe criticism or disapproval (l- a D- u-)

6. successful in earning money (M- t-)

7. a dozen plus one; a group of thirteen (b- d-)

8. threat of great danger (s- o- D-)

9. a complete failure (fi-)

10. laziness; sluggishness; dullness (l-)

Practice Seven:
Matching

Write the word or expression that best matches each definition. Be careful, as the following definitions may be slightly different from the original definitions.

	Definitions	*Words*
_____	**1.** a dozen plus one	**a.** lethargy
_____	**2.** threat of great danger	**b.** investigate
_____	**3.** laziness; dullness	**c.** labyrinth
_____	**4.** place full of blind alleys; a maze	**d.** baker's dozen
_____	**5.** track; examine closely	**e.** sword of Damocles
_____	**6.** book of maps	**f.** Achilles' heel
_____	**7.** weak spot; unprotected place	**g.** Midas touch
_____	**8.** harsh words expressing disapproval	**h.** fiasco
_____	**9.** complete failure	**i.** like a Dutch uncle
_____	**10.** very successful in earning money	**j.** atlas

Practice Eight:
Using the Words

Now can you use the vocabulary words? Answer each question either YES or NO.

1. If a teacher talks to a student like a DUTCH UNCLE, is the teacher scolding that person?   _____

2. Would a quick temper be considered an ACHILLES' HEEL?   _____

3. Would you consult an ATLAS to know where your favorite movie was playing?   _____

4. Would a detective INVESTIGATE a murder?   _____

5. If you fell into a LABYRINTH, would it be easy for you to get out?   _____

6. Would LETHARGY make playing basketball difficult?   _____

7. Would you be happy if your party turned out to be a FIASCO? _____

8. Would a person use the SWORD OF DAMOCLES in a battle? _____

9. Do you think a person without money has the MIDAS TOUCH? _____

10. Do you think giving a customer a BAKER'S DOZEN promotes goodwill? _____

Practice Nine:
Completion

Write the word or expression needed to complete each of the following sentences.

Word List: Achilles' heel, atlas, baker's dozen, fiasco, investigate, labyrinth, lethargy, like a Dutch uncle, Midas touch, sword of Damocles.

1. The enemy's _____ was his lack of air power.

2. Hot weather creates a _____ in people that makes work almost impossible.

3. The bazaar was a complete _____ because the rain kept the crowds away.

4. The police decided to _____ the crime.

5. The test hung over his head like a _____ _____ .

6. Every business deal John makes is successful. He has the _____ .

7. Most bagel factories give a _____ _____ for the price of twelve.

8. The professor spoke to his classes _____ _____ because they failed to complete the required work.

9. We take an _____ with us when we travel.

10. It is difficult to find one's way out of a _____ .

Practice Ten:
Review

How many of these CAPITALIZED words have you learned? Next to each number write the letter of the best definition.

_____ **1.** LIKE A DUTCH UNCLE   A. with kind words B. with harsh words C. with soft words

_____ **2.** ATLAS   A. mapmaker B. book of maps C. an image

_____ **3.** INVESTIGATE   A. look into B. guess C. invest

_____ **4.** LABYRINTH   A. a command B. a laboratory C. a maze

_____ **5.** SWORD OF DAMOCLES   A. threat of danger B. magical sword C. sword used in battle

_____ **6.** MIDAS TOUCH   A. successful in earning money B. powerful C. unsuccessful in earning money

_____ **7.** ACHILLES' HEEL   A. large heel B. mean person C. unprotected area

_____ **8.** LETHARGY   A. liveliness B. laziness C. alertness

_____ **9.** FIASCO   A. success B. fun C. failure

_____ **10.** BAKER'S DOZEN   A. one less than twelve B. one more than twelve C. twelve

Practice Eleven:
More Histories

Tracing the history of words is fun. Here are ten words with interesting pasts. Find where they come from. Your dictionary will be very helpful. After you have learned about them, use them in sentences.

1. Adonis   **6.** hockey
2. amazon   **7.** neighbor
3. assassin   **8.** budget
4. bowling   **9.** tawdry
5. curfew   **10.** vandals

Practice Twelve:
Rhyming Definitions

Have fun with rhyming definitions. For example, a wig can be a vain mane while a vacation can be a diversion excursion. Write the word listed below that best matches each definition. Be careful! There are more words listed than definitions.

Word List: boycott, labyrinth, mentor, mesmerize, tantalize, titan

Definition

_____   **1.** trance stance

_____   **2.** flaunting taunting

_____   **3.** wiser adviser

_____   **4.** reliant giant

_____   **5.** no go

You and Deadly Directions

Each day we are all given many directions, orders and instructions.

"Analyze the problem."
"Discuss the situation."
"Prove your point."

These instructions require different responses. Do you know the special type of answer or action needed for each? This chapter will help you to respond accurately.

Practice One:
Context Clues

Read the following sentences. <u>Underline</u> the context clues.

1. DESCRIBE the argument between the father and the son. Tell me exactly what happened.
2. LIST what the son had done to make the father so angry. Mention the things one after another in time order.
3. NAME the son's friends who were also involved.
4. MATCH what the son did with each statement made by the father.
5. ANALYZE the problem that caused this argument. Include all details.
6. DISCUSS actions that might have prevented the fight. Give me your ideas.
7. JUDGE whether the father or the son was wrong.
8. PROVE that both the father and the son acted hastily. Show me the evidence.
9. SUMMARIZE the problem. Be brief.
10. EXPLAIN what you would have done in the same situation. Include the reasons for your choice.

Practice Two:
Definitions

Listed below are definitions for each CAPITALIZED word used in Practice One. Write the CAPITALIZED word that best matches each definition. There is a clue after each definition to help you match words and meaning. Remember to look for context clues in Practice One.

Words   *Definitions*

_____   **1.** examine carefully (an-)

_____   **2.** give a word picture (de-)

_____   **3.** exchange ideas or different opinions about something (dis-)

_____   **4.** make clear by giving facts or reasons (ex-)

_____   **5.** form an opinion (j-)

_____   **6.** name one after another (l-)

_____   **7.** select things that are like one another (m-)

_____   **8.** mention the word by which someone or something is known (n-)

_____   **9.** show the truth of something (p-)

_____   **10.** state briefly the main ideas (s-)

Practice Three:
Matching

Write the word that best matches each definition.

Definitions   *Words*

_____ **1.** talk over   **a.** analyze

_____ **2.** find things that are alike   **b.** prove

_____ **3.** show the truth of something   **c.** discuss

_____ **4.** set down in a certain order   **d.** explain

_____ **5.** state a word by which someone or something is known   **e.** judge

                                                           f. list

                                                           g. match

                                                           h. name

_____ **6.** examine carefully   **i.** describe

_____ **7.** state briefly   **j.** summarize

_____ **8.** give a word picture

_____ **9.** form an opinion

_____ **10.** make clear by giving facts or reasons

Practice Four:
Substituting Words

Read each of the following sentences. Select the word from the list below that is the best substitute for the CAPITALIZED words. Write the word on the line to the left.

Word List: analyze, describe, discuss, explain, judge, list, match, name, prove, summarize.

_____ **1.** PRESENT DIFFERENT OPINIONS ABOUT how a person should locate a job.

_____ **2.** EXAMINE IN DETAIL the problem of finding a good job.

_____ **3.** NAME ONE AFTER ANOTHER the steps you will take to find a good job.

_____ **4.** How would you FORM AN OPINION ABOUT which job would be better for you?

_____ **5.** MAKE CLEAR BY GIVING DETAILS how to fill in a job application.

_____ **6.** GIVE A DETAILED PICTURE how you plan to dress for a job interview.

_____ **7.** MENTION THE WORDS IDENTIFYING some of the tests given at job interviews.

_____ **8.** Some tests for jobs require you to FIND LIKE OR SIMILAR objects and shapes.

_____ **9.** STATE BRIEFLY THE MAIN POINTS IN the process of job hunting.

_____ **10.** How would you SHOW THAT IT IS TRUE that you can do the job?

Practice Five:
Multiple Choice

Write the letter of the definition that best defines each CAPITALIZED word.

Words	_Definitions_
_____ **1.** ANALYZE	A. look at quickly
	B. examine carefully
	C. state briefly
_____ **2.** DESCRIBE	A. give a word picture
	B. give a brief history
	C. list
_____ **3.** DISCUSS	A. set down in order
	B. fit one thing to another
	C. talk over or write about
_____ **4.** EXPLAIN	A. make plain or understandable
	B. solve by arithmetic
	C. prove something is fair
_____ **5.** JUDGE	A. arrange in groups
	B. form an opinion of something
	C. state briefly
_____ **6.** LIST	A. set down in a certain order
	B. fit one thing to another
	C. hear and decide the winner

_____ **7.** MATCH   A. test by experiment

                                         B. select things that are right

                                         C. state briefly

_____ **8.** NAME   A. find the value of something

                                         B. show differences

                                         C. mention the word by which something is known

_____ **9.** PROVE   A. show the truth of something

                                         B. mention

                                         C. find the faults

_____ **10.** SUMMARIZE   A. determine the number

                                         B. talk over at length

                                         C. state briefly

**Practice Six:
Word Families**

    We've been working with ten verbs. What new words can be formed by adding endings, SUFFIXES, to these verbs? Below are listed some of these verbs plus some of the related noun and adjective forms. The new words are CAPITALIZED, and the following abbreviations are used: v. (verb), n. (noun), and adj. (adjective).

1. analyze-v.
    ANALYSIS-n.   a careful examination
2. describe-v.
    DESCRIPTION-n.   a word picture
3. discuss-v.
    DISCUSSION-n.   talking things over and exchanging ideas
4. explain-v.
    EXPLANATION-n.   something that makes an idea clear and understandable
5. judge-v.
    JUDGMENT-n.   the ability to decide wisely
6. list-v.
    LISTING-n.   a name or item in a list
7. match-v.
    MATCHLESS-adj.   having no match or equal
8. name-v.
    NAMELESS-adj.   not able to name or identify
    NAMESAKE-n.   a person named after another person

9. summarize-v.
  SUMMARY-n.   a short statement of the main points of something

Now can you use these new words in the following sentences? Fill in the word that best completes each sentence.

1. You should check your telephone _____ every time the new telephone directory is published.

2. I need an _____ of this question. I don't understand it.

3. Make a _____ of the main points in his argument. Keep your statement as short as possible.

4. This diamond is _____. There is no other like it.

5. The victim gave a _____ of the criminal to the police artist.

6. A person shows good _____ when he considers several different ways to solve a problem.

7. The _____ of the situation with my friend helped me to understand how he felt.

8. The person who gave this donation wishes to remain _____. He doesn't want anyone to know that he is a contributor.

9. The chemist will make an _____ of this food to see if it can cause cancer.

10. The mother gave the baby the same name as his father. The child is, therefore, the father's _____.

Practice Seven:
Review

The definition has been given. Has word A, B, or C been defined? Write the defined word on the line at the left.

_____   **1.** make clear by giving facts or reasons
                  A. explain   B. list   C. match

_____   **2.** form an opinion

   A. judge   B. list   C. match

_____   **3.** examine carefully

   A. name   B. prove   C. analyze

_____   **4.** mention the word by which someone or

   something is known

   A. judge   B. name   C. explain

_____   **5.** state the main ideas briefly

   A. summarize   B. explain   C. describe

_____   **6.** give a word picture

   A. describe   B. judge   C. prove

_____   **7.** show the truth of something

   A. match   B. summarize   C. prove

_____   **8.** select things that are alike

   A. describe   B. match   C. list

_____   **9.** exchange ideas

   A. prove   B. discuss   C. judge

_____   **10.** name one after another

   A. list   B. match   C. describe

Practice Eight:
Context Clues

Read the following sentences. Underline the context clues.

1. CITE statements from school records that prove your school offers a well-rounded course of study.
2. COMPARE the courses offered by your school with those offered by business and vocational schools. How are they alike?
3. CONTRAST the suggestions made by students and those made by school board members. In what ways are they different? In what ways are they similar?
4. CRITICIZE the methods used to prevent destruction of school property and suggest better methods.
5. DEFINE freedom of speech. What does it mean?
6. ENUMERATE the steps that must be taken to get student ideas approved by the school board. List them one after another in time order.

7. EVALUATE how well the administration handles problems. In your opinion, are problems handled well?
8. IDENTIFY the members of the school board. List their names.
9. JUSTIFY why students should be permitted to take part in school board meetings. Give several reasons.
10. SOLVE the problem of how to provide a school program that will better prepare students for the business world. What is your answer to this problem?

Practice Nine:
Definitions

    Listed below are definitions for each capitalized word used in Practice Eight. Write the CAPITALIZED word that best matches each definition. There is a clue after each definition to help you match words and meanings. Remember to look for context clues in Practice Eight.

Words	*Definitions*
_____	1. state or quote as proof (ci-)
_____	2. show likenesses or similarities and also differences (com-)
_____	3. show differences when compared (con-)
_____	4. find fault (cr-)
_____	5. state the meaning of a word or group of words (d-)
_____	6. list or name things one by one (en-)
_____	7. form an opinion about the quality or value of something (ev-)
_____	8. recognize or name someone or something as a particular person or thing (id-)
_____	9. supply good reasons; show to be just and fair (j-)
_____	10. find the answer to a problem (s-)

Practice Ten:
Matching

Write the word that best matches each definition.

	Definitions	*Words*
_____	**1.** show likenesses and differences	**a.** cite
_____	**2.** list one after another	**b.** compare
_____	**3.** show to be just and fair	**c.** contrast
_____	**4.** give the meaning of a word	**d.** criticize
_____	**5.** judge the importance or value of something	**e.** define
_____	**6.** name or recognize someone or something	**f.** enumerate
_____	**7.** mention or quote as proof	**g.** evaluate
_____	**8.** find the answer to a problem	**h.** identify
_____	**9.** find fault	**i.** justify
_____	**10.** show differences when compared	**j.** solve

Practice Eleven:
Substituting Words

Read each of the following sentences. Select the word from the list below that is the best substitute for the CAPITALIZED words. Write the word on the line to the left.

Word List: cite, compare, contrast, criticize, define, enumerate, evaluate, identify, justify, solve.

_____ **1.** Can you FIND THE ANSWER TO the following crime?

_____ **2.** GIVE THE NAME OF the victim.

_____ **3.** NAME ONE BY ONE the clues that have been found.

_____   4. MENTION AS AN EXAMPLE
                                     another case that is like this
                                     one.

_____   5. POINT OUT THE SIMILAR-
                                     ITIES IN the two crimes.

_____   6. POINT OUT THE DIFFER-
                                     ENCES IN the methods used
                                     by you and by the detective.

_____   7. POINT OUT THE FAULTS
                                     OF the detective's methods.

_____   8. STUDY AND FORM AN
                                     OPINION ABOUT the two
                                     methods.

_____   9. SUPPLY GOOD REASONS
                                     FOR your choice of methods.

_____   10. STATE THE MEANING OF
                                     the charge "murder one."

Practice Twelve:
Multiple Choice

Write the letter of the definition that best matches each CAPITALIZED word.

Words	*Definitions*
_____ **1.** CITE	A. test by experiment
	B. arrange in groups
	C. state or quote as proof
_____ **2.** COMPARE	A. show likenesses and differences
	B. mention
	C. decide or settle
_____ **3.** CONTRAST	A. show differences
	B. state briefly
	C. make the meaning clear
_____ **4.** CRITICIZE	A. count one by one
	B. find fault
	C. show the need for

_____ **5.** DEFINE   A. give an opinion

B. direct attention to

C. state the meaning of

_____ **6.** ENUMERATE   A. list or name one by one

B. picture in words

C. give an opinion

_____ **7.** EVALUATE   A. repeat a statement

B. judge the importance or value of

C. prove incorrect

_____ **8.** IDENTIFY   A. find out by using arithmetic

B. free from blame

C. recognize or name something

_____ **9.** JUSTIFY   A. talk over

B. state the meaning of

C. supply good reasons

_____ **10.** SOLVE   A. find the answer

B. talk over

C. arrange in groups

Practice Thirteen:
Word Families

Once again we've been working with verbs. By adding endings, suffixes, to these verbs we can form new words. Below are listed some of these verbs plus their related noun and adjective forms. The new words are CAPITALIZED, and the following abbreviations are used: v. (verb), n. (noun), and adj. (adjective).

1. cite-v.
CITATION-n.   an award for bravery
                       a summons to appear in court

2. compare-v.
COMPARABLE-adj.   similar
COMPARISON-n.   the act of pointing out likeness

3. criticize-v.
CRITICAL-adj.   inclined to find fault
CRITICISM-n.   faultfinding

4. define-v.
DEFINITE-adj.   clearly defined; exact

5. evaluate-v.
   EVALUATION-n.   forming an opinion about the value of
                          something
6. identify-v.
   IDENTIFICATION-n.   something used to prove who one is
7. justify-v.
   JUSTIFICATION-n.   good reasons for supplying something
8. solve-v.
   SOLUTION-n.   the answer to a problem

Now can you use these new words in the following sentences? Fill in the word that best completes each sentence.

1. During my vacation I tried to convince a friend that we should help fight a forest fire. He was very _____ of the idea. He disapproved and found fault with every reason I gave him.

2. His disapproval only convinced me I was right. His _____ did not stop me.

3. I had been a volunteer fireman at home. This was my _____ for offering to help. I thought it was a good reason.

4. I stated that fighting this fire would be similar to fighting fires at home. I felt they were _____ activities.

5. My friend disagreed. He claimed they were not alike. He stated there was no _____ between fighting city fires and forest fires.

6. The _____ to our problem was to ask the forest ranger if he could use our help. We would let him decide this problem.

7. First the ranger asked us for some sort of _____ _____ to prove our age.

8. Then he made an _____ of our fire-fighting experience. He said this training would be very valuable.

9. Finally he told us exactly where to work. We got a _____ job to do.

10. Because we helped, we both were given awards. I am very proud of my _____.

Practice Fourteen:
Review

The definition has been given. Has word A, B, or C been defined? Write the defined word on the line at the left.

_____ **1.** find fault

A. cite   B. criticize   C. identify

_____ **2.** supply good reason

A. justify   B. solve   C. criticize

_____ **3.** state or quote as proof

A. solve   B. cite   C. contrast

_____ **4.** form an opinion about the quality or value of something

A. cite   B. criticize   C. evaluate

_____ **5.** show differences when compared

A. identify   B. enumerate   C. contrast

_____ **6.** recognize or name someone

A. identify   B. enumerate   C. cite

_____ **7.** name or list one after another

A. evaluate   b. enumerate   C. justify

_____ **8.** find the answer to a problem

A. criticize   B. define   C. solve

_____ **9.** show likenesses and also differences

A. justify   B. compare   C. criticize

_____ **10.** state the meaning of a word

A. define   B. enumerate   C. evaluate

Practice Fifteen:
Reversals

Have you ever looked at a word and then spelled it backwards to form another word? Listed below are a pair of definitions of these kinds of words. For example, the number that comes after nine when reversed is a mesh fabric: TEN—NET.

How many of these can you identify? Write your answers for each pair of definitions in Column A and Column B.

Column A	Column B		
1. _____ _____	**a.** flesh		**a.** a sports group

2. _____ _____ **b.** part of a house   **b.** fasten a boat

3. _____ _____ **c.** thin metal   **c.** louse egg

4. _____ _____ **d.** emergency   **d.** dog bite
                                   button

5. _____ _____ **e.** end   **e.** part of the
                                          peach you don't
                                          eat

6. _____ _____ **f.** opposite of the   **f.** pan
                                   bottom

7. _____ _____ **g.** super scoopers   **g.** nosy people

8. _____ _____ **h.** did evil   **h.** boy's name that
                                               rhymes with
                                               menace

9. _____ _____ **i.** students   **i.** opposite of slip
                                               down

10. _____ _____ **j.** bad, wicked   **j.** not dead

Practice Sixteen:
Colorful
Expressions

Our language contains many IDIOMS, colorful expressions that have unusual meanings. These meanings are not directly related to the meanings of the individual words composing the expressions.

Do you know the meanings of the CAPITALIZED IDIOMS in the following sentences? Rewrite each sentence. Replace the CAPITALIZED words with other words so that the meaning of each sentence is clear. The context should give you a clue to the meaning of each idiom. For additional help, use the dictionary.

1. Don't give up now. Let's GO FOR BROKE.

_____

2. The boss gave me the GO-AHEAD on the project. I start tomorrow.

_____

3. Keep trying. Don't let all your work GO DOWN THE DRAIN.

_____

4. I like your idea. I'll GO TO BAT FOR YOU at the meeting tomorrow.

_____

5. That's one possible answer, but I think I can GO YOU ONE BETTER.

_____

Practice Seventeen:
More Colorful Expressions

    The five IDIOMS in Practice Sixteen are just a few of the idioms in our language which include the word GO. Select from your dictionary five more idioms that include the word GO. Use each in a sentence. Include CONTEXT CLUES to make the meaning of each idiom clear.

1. _____

2. _____

3. _____

4. _____

5. _____

You and Sports

Read the following. Notice the CAPITALIZED words. <u>Underline</u> the context clues that help you understand the meanings of the CAPITALIZED words.

Football: Red versus Blue

This has been a great preseason scrimmage. The Red Team DOMINATED the action in the first half. The score is 30–14. The Red players ANTICIPATE a sweeping victory.

The Blue Team hasn't been able to COMPENSATE for its lack of weight. It had counted on speed to make up for this disadvantage, but so far it hasn't worked.

There's the second-half kick-off. It's a beautiful boot to the eight. Number 13 has been CONSISTENTLY successful in getting the pigskin downfield. He's done it on every kickoff.

The receiver has it! He's picking up yardage but is being PURSUED closely. Number 22 makes the tackle.

Wait a minute. Time has been called. The trainer is going out. The receiver was shaken up on that play. They've got him up, but he seems DISORIENTED and confused. He's being helped off the field.

This is a big loss to the Red Team. The receiver had made a SUCCESSION of great plays, one right after the other.

There's the pass. Hold on! There's been an INTERCEPTION. Blue Team's captain grabbed the ball and is headed for the goal line. He's going all the way for a touchdown.

Number 8 is coming in for the CONVERSION. The kick is good and the fans are going wild. The score is now Red 30 and Blue 21.

Both of these teams will be strong CONTENDERS in the regular season. Neither will give up the fight.

How good a detective are you? Did you recognize the context clues? Listed below are definitions. Write the CAPITALIZED word in Practice One that best matches each definition. There is a clue after each definition to help you match words and meanings. Remember that you can also look at Practice One for context clues.

Words	*Definitions*
_____	**1.** expect or look forward to (a-)
_____	**2.** make up for; also pay (com-!)
_____	**3.** repeatedly, over and over again (cons-)
_____	**4.** people and teams who try to win; competitors (cont-)
_____	**5.** in football, scoring the extra point after a touchdown; in more general use, a change in condition or use (conv-)
_____	**6.** lost one's sense of direction (dis-)
_____	**7.** controlled by superior power (dom-)
_____	**8.** the act of stopping or seizing on the way (in-)
_____	**9.** followed in order to catch; chased (p-)
_____	**10.** a series; one thing coming right after another (s-)

Practice Three:
Matching

Write the word that best matches each definition.

	Definitions	*Words*
_____	**1.** control	**a.** anticipate
_____	**2.** the act of seizing	**b.** compensate
_____	**3.** confused	**c.** consistently
_____	**4.** expect	**d.** contender
_____	**5.** a series	**e.** conversion
_____	**6.** competitor	**f.** disoriented
_____	**7.** chase	**g.** dominate

_____ **8.** pay for   **h.** interception

_____ **9.** a change   **i.** pursue

_____ **10.** repeatedly   **j.** succession

Practice Four:
Using the Words

Write the CAPITALIZED word that correctly answers each of the following questions.

_____ **1.** That play has worked repeatedly. Has it been successful CONSISTENTLY or in CONVERSION?

_____ **2.** The safety caught the ball meant for the wide receiver. Did the safety make an INTERCEPTION or a CONVERSION?

_____ **3.** The place kicker scored the extra point after the touchdown. Did he make the INTERCEPTION or the CONVERSION?

_____ **4.** The quarterback called a series of successful plays. Were the plays in CONVERSION or in SUCCESSION?

_____ **5.** I expect the Steelers to beat the Oilers. Do I PURSUE or ANTICIPATE the victory?

_____ **6.** I think that Pittsburgh and Dallas will be the teams playing against each other in the Super Bowl. Will they be CONTENDERS or CONVERSIONS?

_____   **7.** Houston was overpowered in the first quarter. Were they PURSUED or DOMINATED?

_____   **8.** The running back was followed closely by the defenders. Was the running back PURSUED or DOMINATED?

_____   **9.** A player who is tackled hard may lose his sense of direction for a short period. Is he DOMINATED or DISORIENTED?

_____   **10.** The team's passing ability will more than make up for lack of running power. Will this skill in passing DOMINATE or COMPENSATE for lack of speed?

Practice Five:
Using the Words Again

You have used these words as they are used in sports. Now try using them in sentences not discussing sports. Write the CAPITALIZED word that correctly answers each of the following questions.

_____   **1.** This winter I've had one cold right after another. Have I had a CONVERSION of colds or a SUCCESSION of colds?

_____   **2.** The secret government papers were stolen by the enemy agent before they reached the President. Was this an INTERCEPTION or a CONVERSION of the papers?

—————————————————

—————————————————

—————————————————

—————————————————

—————————————————

—————————————————

—————————————————

3. I lost my way in the forest. I kept walking in circles. Was I PURSUED or DISORIENTED?

4. I seem to make that same mistake over and over. Do I do it in CONVERSION or do I do it CONSISTENTLY?

5. I expect a telephone call. Do I DOMINATE or ANTICIPATE a telephone call?

6. I ran toward my home because I feared that someone was after me. Was I afraid that I was being ANTICIPATED or PURSUED.

7. We liked our house better after we changed it from a one-family to a two-family house. Did we like the SUCCESSION or the CONVERSION?

8. I was afraid not to do what my friends told me to do. Was I COMPENSATED or DOMINATED by my friends?

9. Mary and I are applying for the same job. Are we CONTENDERS for the same job or are we making an INTERCEPTION for the same job?

10. The company has agreed to pay me for my extra work. Did they agree to COMPENSATE me or to PURSUE me?

Practice Six:
Multiple Choice

How many CAPITALIZED words have you learned? Next to each number write the letter of the best definition.

Words   *Definitions*

_____ **1.** DOMINATED   A. lost
                                                    B. controlled
                                                    C. demanded

_____ **2.** ANTICIPATE   A. control
                                                    B. follow
                                                    C. expect

_____ **3.** COMPENSATE   A. make up for
                                                    B. change
                                                    C. throw out

_____ **4.** CONSISTENTLY   A. regularly
                                                    B. occasionally
                                                    C. firmly

_____ **5.** PURSUED   A. led
                                                    B. followed
                                                    C. took

_____ **6.** DISORIENTED   A. confused
                                                    B. contented
                                                    C. calm

_____ **7.** SUCCESSION   A. series
                                                    B. collection
                                                    C. struggle

_____ **8.** INTERCEPTION   A. the act of seizing something
                                                    B. the act of finding something
                                                    C. the act of wanting something

_____ **9.** CONVERSION   A. series
                                                    B. original
                                                    C. change

_____**10.** CONTENDER   A. one who gives up
                                                    B. one who tries to win
                                                    C. one who is in charge

Practice Seven:
Word Families

Our vocabulary can be expanded by adding or subtracting word endings. Here are some new entries for your word bank. The new words are CAPITALIZED, and the following definitions are used: v. (verb), n. (noun), adj. (adjective), and adv. (adverb).

1. anticipate-v.
   ANTICIPATION-n.   hope, expectation
2. compensate-v.
   COMPENSATION-n.   payment
3. consistently-adv.
   CONSISTENT-adj.   always the same
   CONSISTENCY-n.   always behaving or thinking in the same way
4. contender-n.
   CONTEND-v.   struggle or compete for something
5. conversion-n.
   CONVERT-v.   change
6. disoriented-v.
   DISORIENTATION-n.   confusion
7. dominate-v.
   DOMINATION-n.   rule, control
8. interception-n.
   INTERCEPT-v.   stop or seize
9. succession-n.
   SUCCESSOR-n.   a person that follows and takes another's place

Now can you use these new words? Write the word needed to complete each of the following sentences. Don't forget to use the context clues to help you select the right word.

1. The team's owner never allowed the coach to make his own decisions. This _____ of the owner finally made the coach resign.

2. How many people do you think will _____ for his job?

3. After the coach quit, several people applied for his job. Who do you think his _____ will be?

4. It's hard to _____ a losing team into a winning one.

5. The _____ a pro football player receives is high. He earns a good salary.

6. When I ask the coach if I can skip practice, he always says, "No." His answer is certainly _____.

7. Only _____ could make a player run toward the wrong goal.

8. See if the rookie can _____ the ball before it reaches the receiver.

9. I am looking forward to the football game with _____ _____. I hope our seats are good.

10. That quarterback can always be counted on for a good game. His playing shows _____.

**Practice Eight:
Review**

In this practice you have been given the definition. Has word A, B, or C been defined? Write the defined word on the line.

_____ **1.** make up for

A. compensate   B. anticipate

C. dominate

_____ **2.** the act of stopping or seizing

A. conversion   B. compensation

C. interception

_____ **3.** a change in a condition or use

A. disorientation   B. succession

C. conversion

_____ **4.** chase

A. dominate   B. pursue

C. intercept

_____ **5.** always the same

A. consistent   B. disoriented

C. anticipated

_____ **6.** confused; mixed up

A. converted   B. disoriented

C. dominated

_____ **7.** struggle or compete for something

A. dominate   B. contend

C. anticipate

      8. look forward to

          A. anticipate   B. pursue

          C. compensate

      9. a series; one thing coming right

          after another

          A. domination   B. compensation

          C. succession

     10. control

          A. convert   B. dominate

          C. intercept

Practice Nine:
Context Clues

Read the following. Notice the CAPITALIZED words. Underline the context clues that help you understand the meanings of the CAPITALIZED words.

The County Baseball Championship

Central High School's varsity team is playing for the county championship. Their OPPONENT is South High School. TENSION is running high between the two teams. Both coaches fear a fight will break out because of emotional strain on the players.

Unfortunately, a feeling of IMPENDING defeat hangs over the Central team. All year their team has been PLAGUED by injuries. Some of the players are still bothered by sprains and bruises.

Central also lacks the INCENTIVE to win. They've lost the spirit to try just a little bit harder.

In addition, during the third inning, Central had a rough break. Its first baseman was EJECTED from the game. He pushed an umpire during an argument and was ordered off the field.

Since then, every Central player has been completely DEJECTED. We've never before witnessed such low spirits.

In spite of all this, the score is tied: 1–1. It's been a pitcher's battle all the way. Now it's the bottom of the ninth with two out. South is at bat.

What's this? The coach is signaling the pitcher to walk the next batter. That's a bad mistake. Central's coach really ERRED on that one.

With a man on first, the DESIGNATED hitter is coming up. He was picked to bat for the pitcher because of his .350 average.

There's the first pitch. He takes a good cut and connects. It's going right out of the park.

Final score is South 3 and Central 1. South is PROCLAIMED the county champions. The official announcement is being made now by the Mayor.

Practice Ten:
Definitions

Listed below are definitions. Write the CAPITALIZED word in Practice Nine that best matches each definition. There is a clue after each definition to help you match words and meanings. Look at Practice Nine for context clues.

<table>
<tr><th>Words</th><th>Definitions</th></tr>
<tr><td>_____</td><td>1. depressed, sad (dej-)</td></tr>
<tr><td>_____</td><td>2. selected to bat for the pitcher; more generally selected for a special job (des-)</td></tr>
<tr><td>_____</td><td>3. thrown out (ej-)</td></tr>
<tr><td>_____</td><td>4. made a mistake (er-)</td></tr>
<tr><td>_____</td><td>5. threatening or about to happen (im-)</td></tr>
<tr><td>_____</td><td>6. the desire to work harder (in-)</td></tr>
<tr><td>_____</td><td>7. a team or person who tries to win in any situation (op-)</td></tr>
<tr><td>_____</td><td>8. troubled or annoyed (pl-)</td></tr>
<tr><td>_____</td><td>9. announced officially (pr-)</td></tr>
<tr><td>_____</td><td>10. emotional or mental strain (t-)</td></tr>
</table>

Practice Eleven:
Matching

Write the word that best matches each definition.

<table>
<tr><th></th><th>Definitions</th><th>Words</th></tr>
<tr><td>_____</td><td>1. made a mistake</td><td>a. dejected</td></tr>
<tr><td>_____</td><td>2. the desire to work harder</td><td>b. designated</td></tr>
<tr><td>_____</td><td>3. officially announced</td><td>c. ejected</td></tr>
<tr><td>_____</td><td>4. depressed, sad</td><td>d. erred</td></tr>
<tr><td></td><td></td><td>e. impending</td></tr>
</table>

_____ **5.** troubled or annoyed   **f.** incentive

_____ **6.** strain   **g.** opponent

_____ **7.** thrown out   **h.** plagued

_____ **8.** a team or person who   **i.** proclaimed

         tries to win   **j.** tension

_____ **9.** selected

_____ **10.** threatening

Practice Twelve:
Using the Words

Write the CAPITALIZED word that correctly answers each of the following questions.

_____ **1.** The team has been troubled with injuries. Have the players been DEJECTED by injuries or PLAGUED by injuries?

_____ **2.** The team was unhappy after losing such a close game. Was the team DEJECTED or EJECTED?

_____ **3.** A threatening storm made the spectators wear raincoats. Was the storm IMPENDING or PROCLAIMED?

_____ **4.** The catcher was selected for the cleanup spot. Was the catcher DESIGNATED or EJECTED?

_____ **5.** With the score tied and two out, the batter is under a great deal of mental and emotional strain. Is the batter PLAGUED or under TENSION?

_____

_____

_____

_____

_____

6. On this road trip the Yankees will be trying to beat Boston. Will Boston be an OPPONENT or an INCENTIVE?

7. The outfielder threw to second when there was a sure out at third. Did he ERR in his decision or did he PROCLAIM his decision?

8. It was officially announced that the pitcher had won the Most Valuable Player award. Was the pitcher told he was the IMPENDING winner or was he PROCLAIMED the winner?

9. Every member of the team had the desire to win. Did the players have the INCENTIVE or the TENSION to win?

10. The team's manager was thrown out of the game for threatening the umpire. Was the manager DEJECTED or EJECTED from the game?

Practice Thirteen:
Multiple Choice

How many CAPITALIZED words have you learned? Next to each number write the letter of the best definition.

Words	Definitions
_____ **1.** OPPONENT	A. winner
	B. loser
	C. competitor

_____	**2.** TENSION	A. calmness
		B. ease
		C. strain
_____	**3.** IMPENDING	A. confusing
		B. threatening
		C. cheering
_____	**4.** PLAGUED	A. confused
		B. annoyed
		C. changed
_____	**5.** INCENTIVE	A. sense
		B. desire
		C. skill
_____	**6.** EJECTED	A. changed
		B. injured
		C. thrown out of
_____	**7.** DEJECTED	A. sick
		B. sad
		C. ashamed
_____	**8.** ERRED	A. made a mistake
		B. made a change
		C. made up for
_____	**9.** DESIGNATED	A. named
		B. made
		C. designed
_____	**10.** PROCLAIMED	A. announced
		B. answered
		C. refused

Practice Fourteen:
Word Families

Our vocabulary can be expanded by adding new meanings to familiar words and by adding or subtracting word endings. Here are some new entries for your word bank. The new words are CAPITALIZED, and the following abbreviations are used: v. (verb), n. (noun), and adj. (adjective).

1. dejected-adj.
DEJECTION-n.   sadness

2. designate-v.

DESIGNATION-n.   selection; appointment

3. eject-v.

EJECTION-n.   the state of being thrown out

4. err-v.

ERROR-n.   mistake

ERRONEOUS-adj.   containing errors; wrong

ERRATA-n.   a list of errors and their corrections

5. plague-v.

PLAGUE-n.   a serious disease affecting many people

6. proclaim-v.

PROCLAMATION-n.   announcement

7. tension-n.

TENSE-adj.   showing or feeling emotional or mental strain

TENSENESS-n.   strain

Can you use these new words? Write the word needed to complete each of the following sentences.

1. The fielder dropped the ball. This _____ cost the team the game.

2. The player was so _____ that he could not relax.

3. He was celebrating because of his _____ as first-string catcher.

4. Almost   every   player   on   the   team   was   sick.   It   was   like   a _____ .

5. The reporter made an _____ statement about the game. The next day the newspaper printed a correction.

6. The player's _____ showed in his face. It was pale and strained.

7. The _____ by the Commissioner officially announced the changes in the rules.

8. The athlete was very sad when he didn't make the team. Because of his _____ he wouldn't talk to his friends.

9. On the page marked _____ you will find a list of errors and their corrections.

10. The umpire signaled that the player was out of the game. The entire team was angered by the _____ of this player.

Practice Fifteen:
Review

In this practice you have been given the definition. Has word A, B, or C been defined? Write the defined word on the line.

_____ **1.** about to happen

A. designating   B. impending

C. proclaiming

_____ **2.** troubled or annoyed

A. ejected   B. designated   C. plagued

_____ **3.** depressed, sad

A. dejected   B. ejected   C. proclaimed

_____ **4.** emotional or mental strain

A. tension   B. ejection   C. designation

_____ **5.** a team or person who tries to win

A. incentive   B. proclamation

C. opponent

_____ **6.** thrown out

A. dejected   B. ejected   C. erred

_____ **7.** selected for something

A. plagued   B. designated   C. erred

_____ **8.** announced officially

A. proclaimed   B. plagued   C. dejected

_____ **9.** made a mistake

A. ejected   B. erred   C. designated

_____ **10.** the desire to work harder

A. designation   B. proclamation

C. incentive

Practice Sixteen:
Context Clues

Read the following. Notice the CAPITALIZED words. Underline the context clues which help you understand the meanings of the CAPITAL-IZED words.

Basketball: Will You Be Chosen for the Team?

From time to time college coaches visit high schools to RECRUIT outstanding athletes. Good players are always needed on women's as well as men's college teams.

What FACTORS will a coach consider in picking a basketball player? He will notice size and speed as well as AGILITY. A player's ease and quickness of movement are all-important. In addition, a long STRIDE helps the player get down court fast.

The player should also be a high scorer and fast on REBOUNDS, seizing the ball quickly after it hits the backboard. Moreover, a player should have the FACILITY to spot the open forward and use that person to make scoring plays.

A player's TEMPERAMENT is also important. A good disposition helps a player get along well with teammates. Moreover, a successful athlete needs COMPOSURE. Self-control on the court allows a person to plan carefully and play a better game. A good player cannot become FRUSTRATED easily. Feeling discouraged prevents a person from doing his best. Finally, a player needs the ability to CONCENTRATE upon the game and not let his attention wander. This makes the winning combination of skills and personal characteristics.

Practice Seventeen:
Definitions

Listed below are definitions. Write the CAPITALIZED word in Practice Sixteen that best matches each definition. There is a clue after each definition to help you match words and meanings. Remember to look at Practice Sixteen for context clues.

Words	Definitions
_____	1. ease and quickness of movement (a-)
_____	2. self-control (com-)
_____	3. pay close attention to something (con-)
_____	4. ability, skill (f-)
_____	5. qualities (f-)
_____	6. discouraged, defeated (fr-)
_____	7. catching the ball after it bounces off something (reb-)

_____ **8.** get the services of someone (rec-)

_____ **9.** the distance or length of a step (s-)

_____ **10.** disposition or nature (t-)

Practice Eighteen:
Matching

Write the word that best matches each definition.

	Definitions	_Words_
_____	**1.** skill	**a.** agility
_____	**2.** discouraged	**b.** composure
_____	**3.** get the services of a person	**c.** concentrate
_____	**4.** disposition	**d.** facility
_____	**5.** catching after a bounce	**e.** factors
_____	**6.** length of a step	**f.** frustrated
_____	**7.** self-control	**g.** rebound
_____	**8.** qualities	**h.** recruit
_____	**9.** pay close attention	**i.** stride
_____	**10.** ease and quickness of movement	**j.** temperament

Practice Nineteen:
Using the Words

Write the CAPITALIZED word that correctly answers each of the following questions.

_____ **1.** Because the player was over six feet tall, he covered a lot of distance with each step. Did he have a long REBOUND or a long STRIDE?

_____

2. A number of qualities and conditions contributed to the success of the team. Was it a number of FACTORS or RECRUITS that made for a winning combination?

_____

3. The forward's quickness and ease of movement captured everyone's attention. Was it the forward's AGILITY or the forward's TEMPERAMENT that everyone noticed?

_____

4. The athlete's pleasant disposition made him a favorite of the team. Did the athlete have a good FACILITY or a good TEMPERAMENT?

_____

5. The playmaker paid close attention to the position of every person on the court. Did the playmaker CONCENTRATE or FRUSTRATE?

_____

6. The coach wanted the outstanding player to attend Boston University. Did the coach want to FRUSTRATE or RECRUIT the player?

_____

7. The guard's self-control prevented a fight. Was it the guard's AGILITY or COMPOSURE that kept peace on the court?

_____

8. The forward caught the ball as it bounced off the backboard.

Did he get the REBOUND or the RECRUIT?

_____

9. A player cannot allow himself to become defeated and discouraged. If he becomes discouraged, will he be FRUSTRATED or RECRUITED?

_____

10. The forward's skill in shooting baskets helped the team to win the game. Was it the forward's AGILITY or FACILITY in shooting baskets that led to a win?

Practice Twenty:
Multiple Choice

How many of the CAPITALIZED words have you learned? Next to each number write the letter of the best definition.

Words	_Definitions_
_____ 1. RECRUIT	A. judge
	B. watch
	C. get
_____ 2. FACTORS	A. qualities
	B. people
	C. luck
_____ 3. AGILITY	A. speed and ease
	B. carefulness
	C. intelligence
_____ 4. STRIDE	A. distance of a throw
	B. length of a step
	C. support from teammates
_____ 5. REBOUNDS	A. recovering the ball
	B. passing the ball
	C. shooting baskets

_____ **6.** FACILITY   A. intelligence

                                     B. luck

                                     C. skill

_____ **7.** TEMPERAMENT   A. anger

                                     B. disposition

                                     C. calmness

_____ **8.** COMPOSURE   A. temper

                                     B. calmness

                                     C. intelligence

_____ **9.** FRUSTRATED   A. defeated

                                     B. excited

                                     C. angered

_____ **10.** CONCENTRATE   A. to allow one's attention to wander

                                     B. to call the plays

                                     C. to pay close attention

Practice Twenty-One:
Word Families

Our vocabulary can be expanded by adding and subtracting word endings. Here are some new words for your word bank. The new words are CAPITALIZED, and the following abbreviations are used: v. (verb), n. (noun), and adj. (adjective).

1. agility-n.
    AGILE-adj.   able to move or think easily and quickly
    AGILENESS-n.   ease and quickness of movement or thought
2. composure-n.
    COMPOSE-v.   make calm
3. concentrate-v.
    CONCENTRATION-n.   close attention
4. facility-n.
    FACILITATE-v.   make easier
5. frustrated-v.
    FRUSTRATION-n.   the state of feeling discouraged
6. recruit-v.
    RECRUITER-n.   a person who enlists or gets new members
    RECRUITMENT-n.   the act of getting the services of someone
7. temperament-n.
    TEMPER-n.   disposition; anger
    TEMPERAMENTAL-adj.   having a personality that is easily upset

Can you use these new words? Write the word needed to complete each of the following sentences.

1. _____ is an important part of a college coach's job. The team needs new players each year.

2. The athlete's _____ was clear to everyone watching the game. He acted very unhappy and discouraged after missing the foul shot.

3. Being a sports reporter requires _____. He must watch the game closely or he will miss some of the plays.

4. She has a very _____ mind. She can always think of a way to solve the problem.

5. A _____ player who gets excited or upset easily can ruin an entire team.

6. The _____ wanted to know whether the high school all-star would be interested in an athletic scholarship.

7. A player who does not lose his _____ easily will make a good team member. Coaches do not want players who get angry quickly.

8. Please _____ yourself. You are very upset. In your present condition you will not be able to shoot a basket.

9. How can we _____ moving the entire team and all the equipment to the new stadium? We need a simple and easy plan.

10. That athlete's _____ makes me envious. I wish I could move as quickly and easily as she does.

Practice Twenty-Two:
Review

In this practice you have been given the definition. Has word A, B, or C been defined? Write the defined word on the line.

_____ **1.** length of a step
   A. rebound   B. factor   C. stride

_____ **2.** skill, ability
   A. facility   B. factor   C. composure

_____ **3.** catching the ball after it bounces off something

A. recruit   B. rebound   C. facilitate

_____ **4.** self-control

A. composure   B. agileness   C. temperament

_____ **5.** disposition or nature

A. concentration   B. temper   C. temperament

_____ **6.** pay close attention to something

A. facilitate   B. frustrate   C. concentrate

_____ **7.** qualities

A. temperament   B. factors   C. composure

_____ **8.** ease and quickness

A. agility   B. stride   C. rebound

_____ **9.** to get the services of someone

A. rebound   B. recruit   C. compose

_____ **10.** discouraged, defeated

A. concentrated   B. frustrated   C. recruited

You and the Law— Legal Language

We are constantly being bombarded by headlines.

FELONY COMMITTED . . .
POLICE SEEK PERPETRATOR . . .
LOCAL OFFICIAL INDICTED . . .
COUNTERFEIT BILLS FLOODING STORES . . .

How well do we understand these messages?

Practice One:
Context Clues

Read the following selection. Notice the CAPITALIZED words. Underline the CONTEXT CLUES which help you understand the meanings of the CAPITALIZED words.

A Day in Court

As the judge entered, a sheriff's deputy brought a number of people into the courtroom. These people were in CUSTODY because each had been INDICTED for a crime. Some were accused of a FELONY, a serious crime. Others were charged only with a MISDEMEANOR, a lesser crime. In one case, a man charged with murder had been brought to court for ARRAIGNMENT.

As a result of a CIVIL case, not a criminal one, a man was being charged with CONTEMPT of court. According to the charge, he had made threatening remarks when the court announced a JUDGMENT of only $1,000. The man had sued for $100,000, claiming NEGLIGENCE. He believed his employer should have provided a protective guard around a dangerous machine.

These were just a few of the many cases on the court calendar.

109

Practice Two:
Definitions

Listed below are definitions for each capitalized word in Practice One. Write the CAPITALIZED word that best matches each definition. There is a clue after each definition to help you match words and meanings. Remember that you can also look at Practice One for context clues.

Words   *Definitions*

_____ **1.** carelessness (neg-)

_____ **2.** showing no respect for judge or court (con-)

_____ **3.** a serious crime (fel-)

_____ **4.** bringing before a judge to plead guilty or not guilty to a charge (ar-)

_____ **5.** relating to people's private rights (civ-)

_____ **6.** a decision by a court (ju-)

_____ **7.** formally charged with a crime (ind-)

_____ **8.** a minor crime that is not as serious as a felony (mis-)

_____ **9.** official control or care of a person (cu-)

Practice Three:
Matching

Write the word that best matches each definition. The following definitions may be slightly different from the original definitions.

Definitions   *Words*

_____ **1.** protection   **a.** arraignment

_____ **2.** charged; accused   **b.** civil

_____ **3.** a serious crime   **c.** contempt

_____ **4.** a less serious crime **d.** custody

_____ **5.** disobedience   **e.** felony

_____ **6.** neglectfulness   **f.** indicted

_____ 7. hearing a charge and pleading guilty or not guilty

g. judgment

h. misdemeanor

i. negligence

_____ 8. a court decision

_____ 9. relating to people's rights

Practice Four:
Using the Words

Write the CAPITALIZED word that correctly answers each of the following questions.

_____ 1. A prisoner is brought into court to plead guilty or not guilty. Is he brought in for ARRAIGNMENT or CONTEMPT?

_____ 2. A person owes you money and refuses to pay it. You decide to sue. Would this be a CRIMINAL or a CIVIL suit?

_____ 3. A witness refuses to give evidence when the judge orders him to do so. Is this CONTEMPT or CUSTODY of court?

_____ 4. A witness is promised protection by the police. Is he put under protective CONTEMPT or CUSTODY?

_____ 5. The court orders the defendant to pay a settlement of $1,000. Is this decision an ARRAIGNMENT or a JUDGMENT?

_____ 6. Your neighbor does not shovel the snow off his sidewalk. You slip and break an ankle. Do you claim NEGLIGENCE or CONTEMPT?

_____ **7.** Breaking into a bicycle shop and stealing all the bicycles is a serious crime. Is it a MISDEMEANOR or a FELONY?

_____ **8.** The individual was charged with the willful destruction of school property. He was ordered to pay $15.00 damages. Is this a MISDEMEANOR or a FELONY?

_____ **9.** The accused is formally charged with murder by the grand jury. Is he in CONTEMPT or is he INDICTED?

Practice Five:
Multiple Choice

Next to each number write the letter of the definition that best defines each CAPITALIZED word.

Words	_Definitions_
_____ **1.** CUSTODY	A. court
	B. care
	C. criminal
_____ **2.** INDICTED	A. released from court
	B. charged with a crime
	C. worked in court
_____ **3.** FELONY	A. a major crime
	B. a minor crime
	C. no crime
_____ **4.** MISDEMEANOR	A. a major crime
	B. a minor crime
	C. no crime
_____ **5.** CIVIL	A. relating to crime
	B. relating to people's rights
	C. relating to the law

_____ **6.** CONTEMPT   A. disobedience

                                  B. obedience

                                  C. respect

_____ **7.** JUDGMENT   A. a misunderstanding

                                  B. an intelligent person

                                  C. a formal decision

_____ **8.** NEGLIGENCE   A. negativeness

                                  B. carelessness

                                  C. carefulness

_____ **9.** ARRAIGNMENT   A. bringing to court to answer a charge

                                  B. freeing from jail

                                  C. arranging court records

Practice Six:
Word Families

    Our vocabulary can be expanded by adding new meanings to familiar words and by adding or subtracting word endings. Here are some new entries for your word bank. The new words are CAPITALIZED, and the following abbreviations are used: v. (verb), n. (noun), and adj. (adjective).

1. arraignment-n.
    ARRAIGNED-v.   brought to court to hear charges and to plead guilty or not guilty

2. civil-adj.
    CIVIL-adj.   polite
    CIVILIAN-n.   a person not on active duty in a military, fire-fighting, or police force

3. contempt-n.
    CONTEMPT-n.   hatred; disgust
    CONTEMPTIBLE-adj.   worthy of being hated and despised

4. custody-n.
    CUSTODIAN-n.   one who guards and keeps property or records; one who guards prisoners

5. felony-n.
    FELON-n.   a person who commits a serious crime; criminal

6. indicted-v.
    INDICTMENT-n.   a formal statement charging a person with a crime

7. judgment-n.
    JUDICIOUS-adj.   sensible; careful; wise

8. negligence-n.
    NEGLECT-v.   leave undone

Can you use these new words? Write the word needed to complete each of the following sentences.

1. The grand jury handed down an _____ charging the man with murder.

2. The accused will be _____ in this courtroom within a half hour.

3. The DA was the _____ in charge of all records dealing with the case.

4. If he wanted to win his case, he could not _____ to present all of this evidence to the jury.

5. The lawyer advised the prisoner to plead guilty to the lesser charge. He said it would be a _____ move to win his freedom.

6. Although the judge did not like the DA, he was always _____ when he spoke to him.

7. On the other hand, the DA thought the judge was spineless and _____.

8. The _____ was finally convicted and sentenced to life imprisonment.

9. The prisoner showed his _____ for the judge by cursing.

10. One _____ who had been in the court-room was so impressed that he decided to join the auxiliary police department and help protect his neighborhood.

Practice Seven:
Review

In this practice, the definition has been given to you. Has word A, B, or C been defined? Write the defined word on the line.

_____ 1. carelessness

        A. judgment   B. negligence   C. felony

_____ 2. charged with a crime

        A. indicted   B. neglected   C. arraigned

_____ **3.** a minor crime

A. felony B. custody C. misdemeanor

_____ **4.** lack of respect for a court or judge

A. judgment B. contempt C. arraignment

_____ **5.** a major crime

A. misdemeanor B. felony C. custody

_____ **6.** relating to people's rights

A. judgment B. custody C. civil

_____ **7.** official control or care of a person

A. custody B. negligence C. contempt

_____ **8.** a court decision

A. misdemeanor B. felony C. judgment

_____ **9.** bringing before a judge to enter a plea of guilty or not guilty to a charge

A. indictment B. judgment C. arraignment

Practice Eight:
Context Clues

Read the following selection. Notice the capitalized words. Underline the context clues which help you understand the meanings of the CAPITALIZED words.

Returning to the Courtroom

One PERPETRATOR charged with robbery had been EXTRADITED from Chicago to New York City to stand trial. The crime had been committed in New York City. Therefore, Chicago had no JURISDICTION over the case.

Another man accused of LARCENY had stolen $10,000 from a bank. He WAIVED his right to a trial by jury. The judge would decide whether or not he was guilty.

A teenager had ASSAULTED an old man. The victim of the attack was in the courtroom to TESTIFY against the young person.

In a courtroom on the second floor, a SWINDLER had cheated an old man out of his life's savings. This IMPOSTOR had pretended to be a banker.

In the next case a woman had DEFAULTED on a loan. She had failed to make five payments on her car.

A businessman was charged with USURY because he had collected illegally high interest on loans.

Practice Nine:
Definitions

Listed below are definitions for each CAPITALIZED word in Practice Eight. Write the word that best matches each definition. There is a clue after each definition to help you match words and meanings. Remember that you can also look at Practice Eight for context clues.

Words

_____

_____

_____

_____

_____

_____

_____

_____

_____

_____

_____

Definitions

1. made a violent physical attack upon some person (a-)

2. failed to pay or do something (d-)

3. delivered or sent to another state or country where the crime took place (ex-)

4. a person who tricks others by taking someone else's title or name (im-)

5. the place where a person or court has legal authority (j-)

6. the crime of stealing something which belongs to someone else (l-)

7. a person who commits a crime (p-)

8. a cheat who tricks people out of money and other valuables (sw-)

9. make a statement under oath in court; give evidence (t-)

10. illegally high interest charged on borrowed money (u-)

11. gave up (w-)

Practice Ten:
Matching

Write the word that best matches each definition.

	Definitions	*Words*
_____	1. a person who takes the name of someone else	a. assault
_____	2. person who commits a crime	b. default
_____	3. give evidence in court	c. extradite
_____	4. a violent attack	d. impostor
_____	5. give up	e. jurisdiction
_____	6. territory over which a person has authority	f. larceny
_____	7. person who takes by trickery money belonging to someone else	g. perpetrator
_____	8. failure to do something required	h. swindler
_____	9. theft	i. testify
_____	10. to turn over to authorities of the state where the crime was committed	j. usury
_____	11. illegally high interest	k. waive

Practice Eleven:
Using the Words

Write the CAPITALIZED word that correctly answers each of the following questions.

_____ 1. You are asked to make a statement about something you saw. Are you asked to DEFAULT or to TESTIFY?

_____ 2. A person is arrested for attacking another person. Is he charged with LARCENY or ASSAULT?

_____

_____

_____

_____

_____

_____

_____

_____

3. An accused is being tried for bank robbery in the county where you are District Attorney. Is the trial being held in your CUSTODY or in your JURISDICTION?

4. You borrowed money. You do not pay it back on the date it is due. Did you DEFAULT on your agreement or did you WAIVE your agreement?

5. A person commits a crime in New York City. He is caught and arrested in California. Is he EXTRADITED or INDICTED to New York City for trial?

6. A person claims he is a doctor but he has never gone to medical school. Is he a USURER or an IMPOSTOR?

7. A person is accused of stealing a diamond ring. Is he charged with ASSAULT or LARCENY?

8. A person is accused of committing a robbery. Is he called the IMPOSTOR or the PERPETRATOR?

9. A person is accused of tricking his friend into investing money in fake stocks. Is he an IMPOSTOR or a SWINDLER?

10. A person is arrested for having charged illegally high interest on a loan. Is he accused of LARCENY or USURY?

_____ **11.** You voluntarily give up your right to a jury trial. Did you DEFAULT or WAIVE your right?

Practice Twelve: Multiple Choice

Next to each CAPITALIZED word write the letter of the best definition.

Words	*Definitions*
_____ **1.** ASSAULTED	A. murdered B. robbed C. attacked
_____ **2.** DEFAULTED	A. failed to pay B. paid in full C. paid only part
_____ **3.** EXTRADITED	A. sent for trial to a place where crime was committed B. sent home from jail on bail C. freed because found innocent
_____ **4.** IMPOSTOR	A. faker B. an honest person C. a court employee
_____ **5.** LARCENY	A. murder B. robbery C. attack
_____ **6.** JURISDICTION	A. authority to select a jury B. authority to select a judge C. authority to enforce laws
_____ **7.** PERPETRATOR	A. a person who defends a criminal B. a person who commits a crime C. a person who studies law
_____ **8.** SWINDLER	A. a court clerk B. a lawyer C. a thief
_____ **9.** TESTIFY	A. take a test B. give evidence C. be freed
_____ **10.** USURY	A. using others B. abusing others C. charging illegally high interest

_____11. WAIVED   A. said good-bye
                         B. fought hard
                         C. gave up

Practice Thirteen:
Word Families

Here are some more new words. They were formed by adding suffixes or taking away suffixes from the words listed. The new words are CAPITALIZED, and the following abbreviations are used: v. (verb), n. (noun). and adj. (adjective).

1. default-v.
   DEFAULTER-n.   one who fails to make payments on money owed
2. extradite-v.
   EXTRADITION-n. the surrender by the authorities of a person accused of a crime to the state where the crime took place
3. perpetrator-n.
   PERPETRATE-v.   commit (a crime)
4. testify-v.
   TESTIMONY-n.   evidence given in court
5. usury-n.
   USURER-n.   one who charges illegally high interest rates

Now can you use these new words in the following sentences? Fill in the word that best completes each sentence.

1. The _____ was arrested for charging illegal interest.

2. The _____ given by the witnesses proved the man had committed the crime.

3. The _____ of the prisoner from Virginia to Vermont will take place tomorrow.

4. Pay   back   borrowed   money   promptly.   Never   become   a _____ .

5. How could anyone _____ such a horrible crime?

Practice Fourteen:
Verb Suffixes

By adding suffixes to the ends of verbs we can express different times or conditions. Below are listed seven verbs. You have two problems. First, decide from the context clues which verb fits into the sentence. Second, decide whether a suffix has to be added to the verb.

Verbs: assault, default, extradite, perpetrate, swindle, testify, waive.

Verb Suffixes: -s, -ed, -ing.

Sample Sentence: Last week the accused _____ the man with a baseball bat.

The verb that fits the context is ASSAULT. What ending must be added to ASSAULT to make it express past time?

Write the complete word in the sample sentence. The sample sentence should now read:

"The accused ASSAULTED the man with a baseball bat."

1. Each year that employee has been _____ his company out of thousands of dollars.

2. Yesterday the accused was _____ to Florida where the crime was committed.

3. Each week the medical examiner _____ at many trials.

4. Are you _____ on your car payments or are you paying them promptly?

5. The gang _____ a kidnapping that shocked the nation.

Practice Fifteen:
Review

In this practice the definition has been given to you. Has word A, B, or C been defined? Write the defined word on the line.

_____ 1. to give up a right

A. swindle   B. default   C. waive

_____ 2. the area where a person has legal authority

A. testimony   B. larceny   C. jurisdiction

_____ 3. failure to do something

A. default   B. swindle   C. extradite

_____ 4. send to place where crime was committed

A. waive   B. extradite   C. default

_____ **5.** a person who tricks others by taking some one else's name

A. impostor   B. perpetrator   C. usurer

_____ **6.** to give evidence in court

A. perpetrate   B. swindle   C. testify

_____ **7.** a person who commits a crime

A. impostor   B. perpetrator   C. usurer

_____ **8.** a violent physical attack

A. assault   B. default   C. perpetrate

_____ **9.** theft

A. assault   B. larceny   C. default

_____ **10.** illegally high interest

A. extradition   B. larceny   C. usury

_____ **11.** a cheat who tricks others out of money or valuables

A. swindler   B. usurer   C. defaulter

Practice Sixteen:
Powerful Prefixes

A sure way to build your vocabulary is to add a prefix to the beginning of a word to create a new word. The newly created words have different meanings. Here are some prefixes and their meanings:

Prefix	Meaning
il-	in, on, not
un-	not
mis-	wrongly, bad
re-	back, again
dis-	not, opposite
pro-	in favor of

Using a separate sheet of paper, place a prefix in front of each word listed below. Define the new word. Use the dictionary to check your definition. Then use each new word in a sentence.

1. agreement   **6.** judge
2. charged   **7.** legal
3. civil   **8.** place
4. claimed   **9.** inform
5. count   **10.** trial

Practice Seventeen:
**Colorful
Expressions**

Do you know the meanings of the following CAPITALIZED IDIOMS? Rewrite each sentence. Replace the CAPITALIZED words with other words so that the meaning of each sentence is clear.

The context should give you a clue to the meaning of each IDIOM. For additional help, use the dictionary.

1. When the child told his parents about the surprise party, he let the CAT OUT OF THE BAG.

_____

2. His friends ran away and left him HOLDING THE BAG.

_____

3. Did the waitress give you your DOGGY BAG?

_____

4. The candidate knew that winning the election was IN THE BAG.

_____

5. The student studied many hours and developed BAGS under her eyes.

_____

Practice Eighteen:
**More Colorful
Expressions**

The five IDIOMS or colorful expressions in Practice Seventeen are just a few of the IDIOMS in our language that include the word BAG.

Select five IDIOMS or colorful expressions that include the word BULL. You'll find them listed under BULL in your dictionary. Use each in a sentence. Include context clues to make the meaning of each IDIOM clear.

1. _____   _____

2. _____   _____

3. _____   _____

4. _____   _____

5. _____   _____

STEP EIGHT: **You and Advertising**

Practice One:
Context Clues

Read the following advertisement. <u>Underline</u> the context clues that help you to understand the meaning of each CAPITALIZED word.

Why Cook at Home?

The fast-food industry offers—

AUTHENTIC, real American cooking
UNADULTERATED, pure beef
MELLOW, sweet, and juicy burgers
AMPLE servings, delicious and generous
COMPACT containers, neatly and closely organized
INGENIOUS service, skillful and fast
SUBSTANTIAL savings, high quality and low prices

Decor CORRELATED with calm atmosphere
All designed for the DISCRIMINATING customer
UNPARALLELED for quality and price

The best for those who demand the best

Practice Two:
Definitions

Listed below are definitions for each CAPITALIZED word used in Practice One. Write the CAPITALIZED word that best matches each definition. There is a clue after each definition. Remember to look for context clues in Practice One.

Words	*Definitions*
_____	**1.** clever; expert; skillful (in-)
_____	**2.** full-flavored; soft; pleasing (m-)

124

_____   3. distinguished; having excellent taste or judgment (di-)

_____   4. related to one another; interrelated (cor-)

_____   5. plentiful; large; spacious (am-)

_____   6. real; genuine; original (au-)

_____   7. considerable (amount); important (sub-)

_____   8. pure; clear; unmixed; spotless (una-)

_____   9. with no equal or parallel, unmatched (unp-)

_____   10. firmly packed; taking up a small space because of close, orderly arrangement (com-)

Practice Three:
Matching

Write the word that best matches each definition.

	Definitions	*Words*
_____	**1.** pure, unmixed	**a.** substantial
_____	**2.** considerable (amount); important	**b.** correlated
_____	**3.** unmatched; no equal	**c.** authentic
_____	**4.** genuine; real; original; actual	**d.** unadulterated
_____	**5.** large; plentiful; spacious	**e.** mellow
_____	**6.** full-flavored; pleasing	**f.** discriminating
_____	**7.** related to one another	**g.** ample
_____	**8.** having excellent taste or judgment	**h.** ingenious
_____	**9.** clever; skillful	**i.** compact
_____	**10.** firmly packed; taking little space	**j.** unparalleled

Practice Four:
Using the Words

Write the CAPITALIZED word that correctly answers each of the following questions.

_____

_____

_____

_____

_____

_____

_____

_____

_____

1. You are looking for a cheese that is smooth and full-flavored. Do you want a MELLOW or a CORRELATED cheese?

2. Some people have excellent taste and judgment. Do they have COMPACT or DISCRIMINATING taste?

3. When you are decorating your home, do you look for CORRELATED or AMPLE color schemes?

4. Do you find things on sale at MELLOW or SUBSTANTIAL savings?

5. You want a genuine Persian rug. Must it be CORRELATED or AUTHENTIC?

6. Is pure water SUBSTANTIAL or UNADULTERATED?

7. You are looking for a spacious, roomy apartment. Do you want an AMPLE or a COMPACT place?

8. You have just enough money to buy a small, economical car. Will you buy one that is COMPACT or one that is CORRELATED?

9. You have just designed a new filing system for your office. Is

the system DISCRIMINATING or INGENIOUS?

_____ **10.** Is the largest diamond in the world UNPARALLELED or CORRELATED in size?

Practice Five:
Multiple Choice

Next to each number write the letter of the best definition.

Words	*Definitions*
_____ **1.** AUTHENTIC	A. false
	B. inaccurate
	C. real
_____ **2.** UNADULTERATED	A. pure
	B. inferior
	C. harmful
_____ **3.** MELLOW	A. full-flavored
	B. sour
	C. flat
_____ **4.** AMPLE	A. plentiful
	B. limited
	C. sparse
_____ **5.** COMPACT	A. arranged loosely
	B. arranged in a close, orderly way
	C. prearranged
_____ **6.** INGENIOUS	A. clumsy
	B. clever
	C. unresourceful
_____ **7.** SUBSTANTIAL	A. small (amount)
	B. considerable (amount)
	C. insignificant (amount)
_____ **8.** CORRELATED	A. disconnected
	B. opposed
	C. closely related

_____ **9.** DISCRIMINATING   A. showing excellent taste or judgment

B. showing poor taste or judgment

C. showing sadness

_____**10.** UNPARALLELED   A. similar

B. equal

C. unequaled

Practice Six:
Word Families

    Here are some new words all related to the original words in this section. The new words are CAPITALIZED, and the following abbreviations are used: v. (verb), n. (noun), and adj. (adjective).

1. ample-adj.
    AMPLIFY-v.   make stronger and greater
    AMPLIFICATION-n.   an increase in the strength of an electronic sound
2. authentic-adj.
    AUTHENTICATE-v.   show that something is genuine; confirm
3. compact-adj.
    COMPACTOR-n.   machine that crushes garbage and rubbish to reduce its volume
4. unparalleled-adj.
    PARALLEL-adj.   same distance apart everywhere and never meeting
5. correlated-adj.
    CORRELATE-v.   show the connection, the link, between things
6. discriminating-adj.
    DISCRIMINATE-v.   treat a person differently, frequently in an unfair way
    DISCRIMINATION-n.   prejudice
7. mellow-adj.
    MELLOWNESS-n.   in fruits—sweetness and softness because they are ripe
8. substantial-adj.
    SUBSTANTIATE-v.   prove with facts

    Can you use these new words? Write the word needed to complete each of the following sentences.

    1. Is _____ preventing some people from getting the jobs they deserve?

2. Railroad tracks are _____.

3. You must _____ your argument with facts and figures.

4. The fire chief can _____ his voice with a bull horn.

5. The handwriting expert had to _____ the signature on the check.

6. The _____ of the fruit made it soft and sweet.

7. A lawyer must _____ the facts at a trial to show the connection between them.

8. The band's _____ was so loud that we could not hear each other talk.

9. Businesses _____ against women when they pay men more money than women for the same job.

10. A _____ can press garbage into a small package.

Practice Seven:
Review

In this practice the definitions have been given to you. Has word A, B, or C been defined? Write the defined word on the line to the left.

_____ 1. considerable amount; important
   A. compact   B. correlated   C. substantial

_____ 2. plentiful; large; spacious
   A. authentic   B. discriminating   C. ample

_____ 3. soft; pleasing; full-flavored
   A. mellow   B. ingenious   C. ample

_____ 4. firmly packed; taking little space because of close, orderly arrangement
   A. substantial   B. compact   C. correlated

_____ 5. something that has no equal
   A. unparalleled   B. discriminating
   C. unadulterated

_____ **6.** distinguished; having excellent judgment or
taste

A. compact   B. discriminating   C. ample

_____ **7.** skillful; expert; clever

A. correlated   B. compact   C. ingenious

_____ **8.** genuine; original; real

A. authentic   B. ample

C. discriminating

_____ **9.** pure, unmixed, clear

A. ingenious   B. unadulterated

C. compact

_____ **10.** mutually related; interrelated

A. discriminating   B. substantial

C. correlated

Practice Eight:
Context Clues

Read the following advertisement. <u>Underline</u> the context clues which help
you understand the meaning of each CAPITALIZED word.

Looking for a New Car?

Our models have—

STURDY, strong bodies
RESPONSIVE, quick-on-the-pickup engines
EFFICIENT, fast-acting brakes
CAPACIOUS, roomy interiors
LAVISH, rich, plush upholstery
FLEXIBLE, easy steering
OPULENT, rich look
UNIQUE, one-of-a-kind design
RELIABLE, dependable workmanship
OPTIONAL, additional features to choose from

Does this sound like a good buy?
See us for your next car.

Practice Nine:
Definitions

Following are definitions for each capitalized word used in Practice Eight.
Write the CAPITALIZED word that best matches each definition.

There is a clue after each definition. Remember to look for the context clues in Practice Eight.

Words	*Definitions*
_____	1. luxurious, plentiful; without limit (l-)
_____	2. strong; firm; powerful; strongly built (st-)
_____	3. dependable; trustworthy; responsible (rel-)
_____	4. capable; effective; skillful (ef-)
_____	5. allowing a choice; voluntary (opt-)
_____	6. adaptable; pliable; adjustable (fl-)
_____	7. one of a kind; unusual; distinctive; unequalled (u-)
_____	8. rich; wealthy; affluent (opu-)
_____	9. large; spacious; roomy (c-)
_____	10. quick to answer or react; sensitive (res-)

Practice Ten:
Matching

Write the word that best matches each definition.

	Definitions	*Words*
_____	1. plentiful	**a.** responsive
_____	2. allowing a choice	**b.** sturdy
_____	3. effective	**c.** lavish
_____	4. dependable	**d.** opulent
_____	5. strong	**e.** efficient
_____	6. quick to answer	**f.** optional
_____	7. rich	**g.** reliable

_____ **8.** roomy   **h.** flexible

_____ **9.** adaptable   **i.** unique

_____ **10.** one of a kind **j.** capacious

Practice Eleven: Write the CAPITALIZED word that correctly answers each of the follow-
Using the Words   ing questions.

_____ **1.** A woman has just purchased a Rolls-Royce. Would you describe her as FLEXIBLE or OPULENT?

_____ **2.** You have to carry packages and passengers in your car. Do you need a CAPACIOUS or an OPTIONAL car?

_____ **3.** Your new car had a faulty valve which the dealer replaced immediately. Was the dealer RESPONSIVE or FLEXIBLE to your needs?

_____ **4.** Your car won't start. Do you need OPTIONAL or STURDY people to push it to the service station?

_____ **5.** When you buy a used car, is it important to deal with a UNIQUE or a RELIABLE merchant?

_____ **6.** Are car salesmen more effective with the public when they are EFFICIENT or OPULENT?

_____ 7. Would a rich person tend to buy a STURDY or a LAVISH car?

_____ 8. On a new car radial tires are an extra. Are the tires an OPTIONAL or a UNIQUE item?

_____ 9. Does FLEXIBLE or STURDY steering help to relax the driver?

_____ 10. Will this OPULENT or UNIQUE sale be an opportunity to buy an inexpensive car?

Practice Twelve:
Multiple Choice

Next to each number write the letter of the best definition.

Words	Definitions
_____ **1.** STURDY	A. light
	B. fragile
	C. strong
_____ **2.** RESPONSIVE	A. quick to react
	B. slow to react
	C. sensible
_____ **3.** EFFICIENT	A. capable
	B. wasteful
	C. lucky
_____ **4.** CAPACIOUS	A. cramped
	B. roomy
	C. limited
_____ **5.** LAVISH	A. cheap
	B. luxurious
	C. sparing

_____ **6.** FLEXIBLE   A. stiff

B. inelastic

C. adaptable

_____ **7.** OPULENT   A. poor

B. rich

C. confident

_____ **8.** UNIQUE   A. one of a kind

B. common

C. usual

_____ **9.** RELIABLE   A. dependable

B. questionable

C. false

_____**10.** OPTIONAL   A. required

B. compulsory

C. voluntary

Practice Thirteen:
Word Families

Here are some new words related to the original words in this section. The new words are CAPITALIZED, and the following abbreviations are used: v. (verb), n. (noun), and adj. (adjective).

1. capacious-adj.

CAPACIOUSNESS-n.   roominess

2. efficient-adj.

EFFICIENCY-n.   skillfulness, effectiveness

3. flexible-adj.

FLEXIBILITY-n.   ability to change; ability to adjust

4. lavish-adj.

LAVISHNESS-n.   extravagance

5. optional-adj.

OPTION-n.   choice

6. opulent-adj.

OPULENCE-n.   wealth; richness

7. reliable-adj.

RELIABILITY-n.   dependability

8. responsive-adj.

RESPONSE-n.   an answer

9. sturdy-adj.

STURDINESS-n.   firmness

10. unique-adj.

UNIQUENESS-n.   distinctiveness; unusualness

Can you use these words? Write the word needed to complete each of the following sentences.

1. The _____ of the motor was the reason the car raced ahead of the others.

2. We were given the _____ of racing our own car or the company's car. We chose our own.

3. The car in the race was heavy, strong, and firm. This _____ _____ gave the driver the confidence to win.

4. A large, flashy car is often a sign of _____.

5. The car was a red Jaguar with leopard upholstery, fully equipped with every available extra. Such _____ ran the selling price sky-high.

6. _____ of steering is important in stock car racing.

7. The car had a large interior. This _____ appealed to big, heavy people.

8. The mechanic was a quick, skillful worker. This _____ helped him to win many new customers.

9. I wrote to the automobile manufacturer and received an answer the same week. This quick _____ pleased me.

10. You need a car dealer you can depend upon. Check on the dealer's _____ before making a purchase.

**Practice Fourteen:
Antonyms**

An ANTONYM is a word that is opposite or nearly opposite in meaning to another word. For example, UP and DOWN are antonyms. Write the word that is most nearly OPPOSITE in meaning to each CAPITALIZED word.

_____ 1. LAVISH   A. plentiful

                                          B. generous

                                          C. little

_____ 2. EFFICIENT   A. wasteful

                                          B. skillful

                                          C. capable

_____ **3.** OPTIONAL   A. left to one's choice

B. voluntary

C. required

_____ **4.** CAPACIOUS   A. roomy

B. spacious

C. cramped

_____ **5.** UNIQUE   A. unusual

B. ordinary

C. uncommon

_____ **6.** OPULENT   A. wealthy

B. poor

C. rich

_____ **7.** FLEXIBLE   A. easily managed

B. rigid

C. springy

_____ **8.** RELIABLE   A. undependable

B. trustworthy

C. dependable

_____ **9.** STURDY   A. strong

B. weak

C. powerful

_____ **10.** RESPONSIVE   A. slow to answer

B. sharp

C. quick to answer

Practice Fifteen:
Review

In this practice the definition has been given. Has word A, B, or C been defined? Write the defined word on the line to the left.

_____ **1.** spacious; roomy

   A. unique   B. opulent   C. capacious

_____ **2.** quick to answer

   A. responsive   B. efficient   C. optional

_____ **3.** luxurious; plentiful

   A. efficient   B. lavish   C. flexible

_____ **4.** effective

　　A. opulent　B. optional　C. efficient

_____ **5.** left to one's choice

　　A. lavish　B. sturdy　C. optional

_____ **6.** one of a kind

　　A. responsive　B. unique　C. reliable

_____ **7.** rich; affluent

　　A. flexible　B. optional　C. opulent

_____ **8.** easily managed; springy

　　A. reliable　B. flexible　C. sturdy

_____ **9.** dependable

　　A. lavish　B. capacious　C. reliable

_____ **10.** strong

　　A. capacious　B. opulent　C. sturdy

Practice Sixteen:　　　　Each CAPITALIZED word has an ANTONYM, an opposite or a near op-
Antonyms　　　　posite. Write the letter of the antonym next to each CAPITALIZED word.

_____ **1.** UNADULTERATED

　　A. impure　B. honest　C. genuine

_____ **2.** MELLOW

　　A. full-flavored　B. pure　C. harsh

_____ **3.** CORRELATED

　　A. related　B. disconnected　C. parallel

_____ **4.** AUTHENTIC

　　A. original　B. factual　C. imitation

_____ **5.** INGENIOUS

　　A. clever　B. witty　C. unoriginal

_____ **6.** DISCRIMINATING

　　A. having excellent taste　B. having poor taste

　　C. showing prejudice

_____ **7.** UNPARALLELED

　　A. similar　B. different　C. close

_____ **8.** COMPACT

　　A. firmly packed　B. loosely packed　C. an automobile

—————— **9.** SUBSTANTIAL

      A. moderate (amount) B. large (amount) C. small (amount)

—————— **10.** AMPLE

      A. enough B. insufficient C. excessive

Practice Seventeen:
Hidden Words

Can you find the words hidden in the following puzzle? They are located vertically, horizontally, and diagonally. The definitions will give you clues to the hidden words. Circle each word as you find it; one word may overlap another. Then write the hidden word next to its definition.

R	U	Q	S	E	A	V	U	W	X	I	H	B	A	D
B	E	N	C	G	I	M	H	N	K	O	P	L	M	I
F	M	R	A	U	T	H	E	N	T	I	C	T	E	S
I	W	A	H	D	D	B	G	L	F	Y	X	Z	R	C
J	N	L	O	K	U	X	B	U	L	W	P	Q	I	R
A	Z	U	P	W	I	L	R	C	P	O	T	C	U	I
S	U	B	S	T	A	N	T	I	A	L	W	F	O	M
E	A	I	B	A	I	N	G	E	N	I	O	U	S	I
C	M	P	E	H	P	T	B	Q	R	W	E	U	L	N
O	P	V	O	R	I	C	O	M	P	A	C	T	P	A
M	L	E	Z	U	T	X	B	Z	U	R	T	W	F	T
F	E	Y	P	A	R	A	L	L	E	L	N	E	G	E
U	B	I	R	C	O	R	R	E	L	A	T	E	D	H

Definitions	*Words*
1. set apart as different	_____
2. roomy	_____
3. interrelated	_____
4. similar	_____
5. genuine	_____
6. firmly packed	_____
7. clever	_____
8. full-flavored	_____
9. large (amount)	_____
10. unmixed	_____

Practice Eighteen:
Scrambled Words

Can you unscramble the mystery word in each sentence? A CONTEXT CLUE is included to help you. Write the mystery word on the line provided.

_____

_____

_____

_____

_____

_____

_____

1. The SERVESINOP person is quick to answer.

2. A water hose must be FEL-BELXI so that it can be rolled up.

3. We need a SOUCICAPA truck to transport a houseful of furniture.

4. We returned a toaster to the local store and received a new one. This is a EBALIREL store.

5. We bought a gorgeous VAHSIL carpet.

6. The family has five active children. They need TYURDS furniture that will not break easily.

7. The NETOLUP businessman takes many trips to vacation areas and spends a great deal of money there.

———————————————   8. Color schemes of a car are one of the OTAPOLIN features offered to the buyer.

———————————————   9. The swimmer will be participating in the Olympics. This will be a UEQNUI experience for this young person.

———————————————   10. The NEFIFETIC secretary made all the arrangements for the meeting.

You and Your Health—Medical Language

Practice One:
Context Clues

Read the following. Notice the CAPITALIZED words. <u>Underline</u> the context clues that help you understand their meanings.

Medical Specialists

Many people have a physical examination once a year. An INTERNIST will do this type of examination. If this doctor discovers a problem, he will recommend a specialist.

If the patient has a skin rash, the internist will recommend a DERMATOLOGIST.

If a person has a foot problem, the specialist to see is a PODIATRIST.

When a person breaks a bone, he is sent to an ORTHOPEDIST. Before the bone is set, the RADIOLOGIST supplies X-ray information.

When an operation is needed, the patient goes to a SURGEON. After the operation, the PATHOLOGIST examines the tissues removed.

A woman is cared for by an OBSTETRICIAN when she is expecting a baby. After the baby is born, a PEDIATRICIAN cares for the child.

If the patient has an emotional problem, not a physical problem, a PSYCHIATRIST is the specialist to see.

Practice Two:
Definitions

Listed below are definitions for each CAPITALIZED word in Practice One. Write the CAPITALIZED word that best matches each definition. There is a clue in each sentence to help you match words and meanings. Remember to look for the context clues in Practice One.

Words	*Definitions*
_____	**1.** a skin doctor (d-)

_____ **2.** a doctor who tells you what kind of illness you have (i-)

_____ **3.** a doctor who delivers babies (ob-)

_____ **4.** a bone doctor (or-)

_____ **5.** examines diseased tissue (p-)

_____ **6.** a children's doctor (ped-)

_____ **7.** a foot doctor (pod-)

_____ **8.** a doctor who treats mental sickness (psy-)

_____ **9.** X-ray specialist (rad-)

_____ **10.** a doctor who operates (s-)

Practice Three:
Matching

This is a matching question. Write the word that best matches each definition. Be careful. The definitions may be slightly different from the original definitions.

	Definitions	_Words_
_____	**1.** treats the skin	**a.** obstetrician
_____	**2.** treats children	**b.** radiologist
_____	**3.** fixes broken bones	**c.** psychiatrist
_____	**4.** is a cutup!	**d.** pathologist
_____	**5.** supplies X-ray information	**e.** surgeon
_____	**6.** delivers babies	**f.** orthopedist
_____	**7.** treats the feet	**g.** pediatrician
_____	**8.** treats mental disorders	**h.** internist
		i. podiatrist
_____	**9.** studies body tissue	**j.** dermatologist
_____	**10.** diagnoses illness	

Practice Four:
Using the Words

Now can you use these words? Write the CAPITALIZED word that best answers each of the following questions.

_____

1. Would you take a sick baby to a PEDIATRICIAN or to a DERMATOLOGIST?

_____

2. If you have been feeling depressed and very upset for no reason, would you visit a PSYCHIATRIST or an ORTHOPEDIST?

_____

3. If your friend thought she was going to have a baby, would she visit an OBSTETRICIAN or a PODIATRIST?

_____

4. If you ached all over and had a fever, would you call a SURGEON or an INTERNIST?

_____

5. Is a PEDIATRICIAN or a PATHOLOGIST a doctor who examines diseased tissues?

_____

6. Would a RADIOLOGIST or a SURGEON operate on you?

_____

7. Would an ORTHOPEDIST or a PODIATRIST put a cast on your broken leg?

_____

8. Would a RADIOLOGIST or a PSYCHIATRIST supply X-ray information?

_____

9. If you injured your foot would you be sent to a PEDIATRICIAN or a PODIATRIST?

_____

10. Your complexion is poor. Would you go to a DERMATOLOGIST or a RADIOLOGIST?

Practice Five:
Completion

From the words listed below select the one that best completes each of the following sentences. Write the word in the space provided.

Word List: dermatologist, internist, obstetrician, orthopedist, pathologist, pediatrician, podiatrist, psychiatrist, radiologist, surgeon.

1. An _____ will diagnose an illness.

2. A _____ treats people who are very depressed and upset, but not physically sick.

3. An _____ is a specialist who delivers babies.

4. A _____ is a specialist who cares for children.

5. A _____ treats skin diseases.

6. A _____ treats foot problems.

7. A _____ studies body tissue.

8. An _____ sets broken bones.

9. A _____ is a specialist in performing operations.

10. A _____ supplies X-ray information.

Practice Six:
Multiple Choice

Next to the number of each CAPITALIZED word, write the letter of the best definition.

Words	Definitions
_____ **1.** INTERNIST	A. bone doctor
	B. a skin doctor
	C. a doctor who tells you the kind of illness you have
_____ **2.** DERMATOLOGIST	A. a doctor who tells you what kind of illness you have
	B. a skin doctor
	C. a doctor who operates

_____ 3. PODIATRIST

        A. a baby doctor

        B. a bone doctor

        C. a foot doctor

_____ 4. ORTHOPEDIST

        A. a doctor who treats mental disease

        B. a baby doctor

        C. a bone doctor

_____ 5. RADIOLOGIST

        A. specialist in use of X-rays

        B. specialist in operating

        C. specialist in treating mental sickness

_____ 6. SURGEON

        A. a doctor who delivers babies

        B. a druggist

        C. a doctor who operates

_____ 7. PATHOLOGIST

        A. a foot doctor

        B. a baby doctor

        C. a doctor who examines tissue

_____ 8. OBSTETRICIAN

        A. a doctor who straightens teeth

        B. a doctor who delivers babies

        C. a bone doctor

_____ 9. PEDIATRICIAN

        A. a doctor who treats mental illness

        B. a doctor who operates

        C. a doctor who treats babies

_____ 10. PSYCHIATRIST

        A. a foot doctor

        B. a doctor who treats mental illness

        C. a doctor who operates

Practice Seven:
Word Families

Our vocabulary can be expanded by adding or subtracting word endings. Here are some new entries for your word bank. The new words are CAPITALIZED, and the following abbreviation is used: n. (noun).

1. dermatologist-n.
   DERMATOLOGY-n.   branch of science that deals with the skin
2. internist-n.
   INTERN-n.   student doctor
3. obstetrician-n.
   OBSTETRICS-n.   branch of medicine dealing with childbirth

4. orthopedist-n.
ORTHOPEDICS-n.   branch of medicine that includes correction or cure of deformities and diseases of bones and joints

5. pathologist-n.
PATHOLOGY-n.   branch of science that deals with study of diseases

6. pediatrician-n.
PEDIATRICS-n   branch of medicine that deals with children and their medical problems

7. podiatrist-n.
PODIATRY-n.   branch of science that deals with foot disorders

8. psychiatrist-n.
PSYCHIATRY-n.   branch of medicine that deals with mental sickness

9. radiologist-n.
RADIOLOGY-n.   the science dealing with X-rays

10. surgeon-n.
SURGERY-n.   medical science dealing with treating diseased conditions by operations

Can you use these new words? Write the word needed to complete each of the following sentences. Don't forget to use the context clues to help you select the right word.

1. Many teenagers have acne. Some read _____ books dealing with this skin ailment.

2. _____ has helped doctors understand the nature of diseases.

3. A person has a diseased appendix. _____ will be performed to remove it.

4. A friend has just graduated from medical school. He is now getting more training as an _____ in a hospital.

5. X-ray treatments have helped people live longer. We have the science of _____ to thank for that.

6. _____ has helped us deal more sensibly with mental problems.

7. The doctor cares for young children. His specialty is
_____.

8. My sister is interested in foot disorders. She is going to study
_____.

9. Diseased and malformed hips and joints are being replaced. Great progress has been made in _____.

10. Fathers are now involved in the childbirth procedure. _____ is no longer just a woman's concern.

Practice Eight:
Review

In this practice you have been given the definition. Has A, B, or C been defined? Write the defined word on the line to the left.

_____ 1. a doctor who treats mental disease

A. orthopedist   B. psychiatrist   C. surgeon

_____ 2. a bone doctor

A. obstetrician   B. pathologist   C. orthopedist

_____ 3. a skin doctor

A. dermatologist   B. pediatrician   c. podiatrist

_____ 4. a doctor who studies changes in tissue caused by disease

A. radiologist   B. internist   C. pathologist

_____ 5. a doctor who delivers babies

A. podiatrist   B. dermatologist   C. obstetrician

_____ 6. a baby doctor

A. pediatrician   B. pathologist   C. surgeon

_____ 7. a foot doctor

A. radiologist   B. internist   C. podiatrist

_____ 8. x-ray specialist

A. psychiatrist   B. radiologist   C. orthopedist

_____ 9. a doctor who operates

A. obstetrician   B. pathologist   C. surgeon

_____ 10. a doctor who names your illness

A. dermatologist   B. internist   C. radiologist

Practice Nine:
Context Clues

Read the following sentences. They contain words used every day in hospitals and doctors' offices. Notice the CAPITALIZED words. <u>Underline</u> the context clues that help you understand their meanings.

1. The doctor's DIAGNOSIS will inform the patient about his health problem.
2. The man had a CONCUSSION. His head had been hit in an auto accident.
3. His hand had also been LACERATED by broken glass.
4. During the operation the doctor made an INCISION in the patient's hand. A thin line of blood marked the cut.
5. Previously, the doctor had ANESTHETIZED the area; therefore, the patient felt no pain.
6. She SUTURED the cut to close it.
7. The bleeding from the wound lessened because the blood had begun to COAGULATE.
8. The doctor gave the patient an ANTIDOTE to fight the snakebite poison.
9. The nurse realized that PARALYSIS had set in. The patient was unable to move her legs.
10. The patient's CONVALESCENCE from the accident was rapid because she followed the doctor's orders.

Practice Ten:
Definitions

Listed below are definitions for each CAPITALIZED word in Practice Nine. Write the CAPITALIZED word that best matches each definition. To help you match words and meanings, there is a clue after each definition. Remember that you can go back to Practice Nine for context clues.

Words	*Definitions*
_____	1. made to lose the sense of pain (an-)
_____	2. something that fights poison; a cure (anti-)
_____	3. thicken or clot (coag-)
_____	4. injury or shock to the brain (con-)
_____	5. recovery (con-)

_____ **6.** identification or recognition of
                                    illness (d-)

_____ **7.** a cut with a sharp instrument
                                    (in-)

_____ **8.** tear roughly (lac-)

_____ **9.** inability to move (p-)

_____ **10.** close by sewing (s-)

Practice Eleven:
Matching

Write the word that best matches each definition. The following definitions may be slightly different from the original definitions.

	Definitions	*Words*
_____	**1.** a gradual recovery	**a.** diagnosis
_____	**2.** identification of illness	**b.** concussion
_____	**3.** inability to move	**c.** lacerated
_____	**4.** thicken or clot	**d.** incision
_____	**5.** a medicine that acts against poison	**e.** anesthetized
		f. sutured
_____	**6.** cut made with a sharp instrument	**g.** coagulate
		h. antidote
_____	**7.** torn roughly	**i.** paralysis
_____	**8.** injury of the brain	**j.** convalescence
_____	**9.** deadened to pain	
_____	**10.** closed by stitches	

Practice Twelve:
Using the Words

Select the CAPITALIZED word that best answers each of the following questions:

_____ **1.** Is a wound LACERATED or
                                    COAGULATED when torn by
                                    a rusty nail?

_____ 2. Would you use an ANTIDOTE or a PARALYSIS against poison?

_____ 3. You suddenly cannot move any part of your body. Do you suspect PARALYSIS or DIAGNOSIS?

_____ 4. After an operation a person goes to a nursing home to recover. Is this a period of ANTIDOTE or CONVALESCENCE?

_____ 5. Your sister has a swollen ankle. Will she ask the doctor to give her a DIAGNOSIS or a CONCUSSION?

_____ 6. Has blood SUTURED or COAGULATED when the bleeding stops?

_____ 7. Is a sudden shock to the head a CONCUSSION or an INCISION?

_____ 8. The accident victim is bleeding heavily. Should the wound be LACERATED or SUTURED by the doctor?

_____ 9. When a surgeon makes a sharp, thin cut, does he make an INCISION or a CONCUSSION?

_____ 10. If you cannot feel pain during an operation, have you been ANESTHETIZED or COAGULATED?

Practice Thirteen:
Completion

From the words listed below, choose the one that best completes each of the following sentences. Write the word in the space provided.

Word List: anesthetized, antidote, coagulate, concussion, convalescence, diagnosis, incision, lacerated, paralysis, sutured.

1. The _____ to his head caused him to feel dizzy.

2. The blood began to _____ causing a scab to form.

3. The surgeon _____ the patient so that he would feel no pain.

4. The doctor _____ the wound to close it.

5. Glass had _____ his arm.

6. The physician's _____ proved that Joe had heart trouble.

7. _____ made it impossible for Jim to move his legs.

8. An _____ was made by the surgeon to remove Jean's tonsils.

9. She spent her _____ in Florida.

10. A child had eaten rat poison. The doctor gave him an _____.

Practice Fourteen:
Multiple Choice

Next to the number of each CAPITALIZED word, write the letter of the best definition.

Words	*Definitions*
_____ **1.** ANESTHETIZED	A. made to lose memory
	B. made to lose an arm
	C. made to lose the sense of pain
_____ **2.** ANTIDOTE	A. illness
	B. cure
	C. poison

_____ **3.** COAGULATE   A. thicken

B. flow

C. thin out

_____ **4.** CONCUSSION   A. an injury of the hand

B. an injury of the foot

C. an injury of the brain

_____ **5.** CONVALESCENCE   A. an infection

B. a gradual recovery

C. a violent shaking

_____ **6.** DIAGNOSIS   A. shortness of breath

B. dizziness

C. identification of an illness

_____ **7.** INCISION   A. high blood pressure

B. a cut made with a sharp instrument

C. cutting a tooth

_____ **8.** LACERATED   A. burned

B. treated

C. torn

_____ **9.** PARALYSIS   A. inability to stop shaking

B. infection

C. inability to move

_____ **10.** SUTURED   A. closed

B. opened

C. burned

Practice Fifteen: Word Families

Our vocabulary can be expanded by adding or subtracting word endings. Here are some new entries for your word bank. The new words are CAPITALIZED, and the following abbreviations are used: v. (verb), n. (noun), and adj. (adjective).

1. anesthetized-v.
   ANESTHESIA-n.   pain killer
2. coagulate-v.
   COAGULATION-n.   thickening or clotting

3. concussion-n.
   CONCUSSIVE-adj.   jarring or shaking
4. convalescence-n.
   CONVALESCENT-n.   someone who is recovering from an illness
5. diagnosis-n.
   DIAGNOSE-v.   recognize by signs or symptoms
   DIAGNOSTIC-adj.   relating to careful, critical study of something
6. incision-n.
   INCISE-v.   cut into or carve
7. lacerated-v.
   LACERATION-n.   a rough, jagged tear
8. paralysis-n.
   PARALYZE-v.   make unable to act, function or move
   PARALYTIC-n.   person who is unable to act, function or move
9. sutured-v.
   SUTURE-n.   strand of fiber used to sew part of living body

Can you use these new words in the following sentences? Fill in the word that best completes each sentence.

1. A _____ was needed to close the wound.

2. Polio can _____ a person.

3. She was a _____ in a nursing home.

4. _____ begins when the blood thickens.

5. The _____ eliminated pain during the operation.

6. The doctor will _____ the disease before giving medicine.

7. The dentist will _____ the filling to make it fit the tooth.

8. The construction worker suffered a _____ blow to the head. He was completely shaken by this accident.

9. The painter fell and suffered a _____ of the arm. It was a long jagged tear that required stitches.

10. The patient was given a _____ test for diabetes.

Practice Sixteen:
Review

In this practice the definition has been given. Has word A, B, or C been defined? Write the defined word on the line to the left.

_____ 1. a medicine that fights poison

A. diagnosis   B. concussion   C. antidote

_____ 2. identification of a disease

A. paralysis   B. diagnosis   C. incision

_____ 3. roughly torn

A. lacerated   B. coagulated   C. anesthetized

_____ 4. surgical cut

A. concussion   B. incision   C. convalescence

_____ 5. clot; thicken

A. lacerate   B. suture   C. coagulate

_____ 6. inability to move

A. paralysis   B. antidote   C. coagulate

_____ 7. sewn up or closed

A. lacerated   B. coagulated   C. sutured

_____ 8. gradual recovery

A. diagnosis   B. convalescence   C. incision

_____ 9. made unaware of pain

A. coagulated   B. anesthetized   C. sutured

_____ 10. injury resulting from blow to head

A. incision   B. concussion   C. antidote

Practice Seventeen:
Find the Impostors

Check the professional who is NOT talking about his or her work.

_____ 1. The ORTHOPEDIST described the bone formation of the hip.

_____ 2. The RADIOLOGIST described an operation he had performed.

_____ 3. The PATHOLOGIST bored the group with stories about diseased tissues.

_____ 4. The PEDIATRICIAN gave his experiences with children and their illnesses.

_____ **5.** A SURGEON described his treatment of people with mental disorders.

_____ **6.** The PODIATRIST told us about the foot problems of football players.

_____ **7.** The PSYCHIATRIST talked about his latest operation on a gall bladder.

_____ **8.** The OBSTETRICIAN described in detail the birth of a baby.

_____ **9.** The INTERNIST told us about his latest diagnosis.

_____**10.** The DERMATOLOGIST discussed the use of X rays in science.

Practice Eighteen:
Medical Miracles

Medical miracles happen every day. A young girl has her leg cut off by a fast-moving train and a team of doctors replace that limb so that she can walk again. Who are these people? The medical team included a PLASTIC SURGEON, a MICROSURGEON, a VASCULAR SURGEON, and an OR-THOPEDIC SURGEON. We have learned that the surgeon operates. What is the specialty of each surgeon mentioned? Your dictionary will help you.

Practice Nineteen:
Same Letters—New Word

Rearrange the letters in each word below to form another word.

_____ **1.** drawer

_____ **2.** stared

_____ **3.** hassle

_____ **4.** solemn

_____ **5.** rivels

_____ **6.** despot

_____ **7.** tarred

_____ **8.** prides

_____ **9.** denial

_____ **10.** magnate

STEP TEN: **You and TV**

Practice One:
Context Clues

Read the following selection. <u>Underline</u> the context clues that help you understand the meaning of each CAPITALIZED word.

A TV News Report

This is the 7 P.M. news. Joy ERUPTED today when victory was finally announced. Happy DEMONSTRATORS filled the streets and EXUBERANT crowds rejoiced.

Leaders of the new government, however, are CONCERNED. Because they are worried, they ask citizens to use RESTRAINT and stop all wild celebrations. They fear that lack of self-control will lead to CHAOS.

To avoid disorder, citizens are being asked to RESUME normal activities. People are being told to DISPERSE and get off the streets. They are being URGED to go back to work.

It is hoped that military RESTRICTIONS will not be necessary. Leaders do not want to use the army to limit personal freedom in order to establish peace.

Practice Two:
Definitions

Listed below are definitions for each CAPITALIZED word used in Practice One. Write the CAPITALIZED word that best matches each definition. There is a clue after each definition. Remember to look for the context clues in Practice One.

Words

_____

_____

_____

_____

_____

Definitions

1. poured forth; exploded (e-)
2. self-control (res-)
3. marchers; paraders; protesters (d-)
4. high-spirited; excited; lively (ex-)
5. confusion; disorder (ch-)

156

_____ **6.** pleaded with; requested; coaxed (u-)

_____ **7.** go back to normal activities; take up again (r-)

_____ **8.** scatter, disband; drive off (dis-)

_____ **9.** worried; anxious; uneasy (con-)

_____ **10.** regulations (res-)

Practice Three:
Matching

Write the word that best matches each definition.

	Definitions	_Words_
_____	**1.** confusion; disorder	**a.** demonstrators
_____	**2.** burst forth; exploded	**b.** restraint
_____	**3.** scatter; disband	**c.** erupted
_____	**4.** worried; uneasy	**d.** restrictions
_____	**5.** self-control	**e.** resume
_____	**6.** pleaded with; requested	**f.** disperse
_____	**7.** high-spirited; excited	**g.** concerned
_____	**8.** protesters	**h.** urged
_____	**9.** take up again	**i.** chaos
_____	**10.** regulations	**j.** exuberant

Practice Four:
Using the Words

Write the CAPITALIZED word that correctly answers each of the following questions.

_____ **1.** When victory was announced, the crowd cheered. Has joy ERUPTED or was joy DISPERSED?

_____ **2.** The prime minister wanted people to use self-control. Did he want people to use CHAOS or RESTRAINT?

_____

3. Do DEMONSTRATORS or RESTRICTIONS march, picket, and protest?

_____

4. The students learned that their chosen leader had won the election. Did this happy, excited group give an EXUBERANT or an URGED cheer?

_____

5. While the fighting was going on, there was complete confusion and disorder. Was the country in a period of CHAOS or RESTRICTIONS?

_____

6. The government wanted to pass a law to provide better housing. Were the people CONCERNED or URGED to support this suggestion?

_____

7. Looting was still going on in the city. Would the government be ERUPTED or CONCERNED about this situation?

_____

8. The prime minister has ordered all citizens to return to their jobs. Will the people RESUME or DISPERSE working?

_____

9. Laws and other regulations protect people and their property. Are these laws RESTRICTIONS or CHAOS?

_____

10. If a crowd is becoming angry and violent, do you want the group to RESUME or to DISPERSE?

Practice Five:
Multiple Choice

Next to each CAPITALIZED word write the letter of the best definition.

Words	Definitions
_____ 1. ERUPTED	A. announced
	B. burst forth
	C. held back
_____ 2. DEMONSTRATORS	A. marchers
	B. police
	C. military leaders
_____ 3. EXUBERANT	A. dull
	B. high-spirited
	C. unhappy
_____ 4. CONCERNED	A. not interested
	B. unrelated to
	C. worried
_____ 5. RESTRAINT	A. self-control
	B. fear
	C. lack of self-control
_____ 6. CHAOS	A. order
	B. system
	C. confusion
_____ 7. RESUME	A. go back to normal activities
	B. stop normal activities
	C. limit normal activities
_____ 8. DISPERSE	A. gather
	B. assemble
	C. scatter
_____ 9. URGED	A. forced to
	B. pleaded with
	C. prevented from
_____10. RESTRICTIONS	A. extensions
	B. controls
	C. hopes

Practice Six:
Word Families

Here are some more new words. They were formed by adding suffixes or taking away suffixes from the words listed. The new words are CAPITALIZED, and the following abbreviations are used: v. (verb), n. (noun), and adj. (adjective).

1. chaos-n.
CHAOTIC-adj.   completely confused or disordered
2. concerned-v.
CONCERN-n.   worry, uncertainty
3. demonstrators-v.
DEMONSTRATE-v.   show, reveal, display
4. disperse-v.
DISPERSAL-n.   scattering, distribution
5. erupted-v.
ERUPTION-n.   outburst; outbreak
6. exuberant-adj.
EXUBERANCE-n.   enthusiasm; energy; spirit
7. restrictions-n.
RESTRICT-v.   limit; confine
8. resume-v.
RESUMPTION-n.   beginning again
9. urged-v.
URGENT-adj.   needing immediate attention
URGENCY-n.   the state of needing immediate attention

Can you use these new words? Write the word needed to complete each of the following sentences.

1. The government had collapsed. There were riots in the streets. This _____ condition continued until a new government was formed yesterday.

2. The officials of the new government met immediately. The _____ of the situation required that the members work right through the night.

3. A crowd gathered to cheer the new officials. The _____ of the people showed their support for the government.

4. The prime minister appeared to talk to the crowd. The worried look on his face revealed his _____.

5. He announced to the people that he would _____ their freedom with a 6 P.M. curfew.

6. The army has been ordered to break up all street gatherings. This show of force will _____ the power of the government.

7. All weapons will be taken away from the citizens. A future _____ of violence seems impossible.

8. The electric plant was destroyed during the fighting. An _____ appeal has been made for volunteers to help rebuild it.

9. An immediate _____ of money will be made to care for children left without homes.

10. With the _____ of business activity the country is once again peaceful and calm.

Practice Seven:
Review

In this practice the definition has been given to you. Has word A, B, or C been defined? Write the defined word on the line to the left.

_____ 1. disband; scatter

A. disperse   B. resume   C. restrict

_____ 2. uneasy; worried

A. demonstrated   B. concerned   C. restrained

_____ 3. disorder

A. restraint   B. exuberance   C. chaos

_____ 4. show; reveal

A. demonstrate   B. disperse   C. restrain

_____ 5. take up again

A. restrict   B. restrain   B. resume

_____ 6. self-control

A. eruption   B. restraint   C. exuberance

_____ 7. excited; lively

A. exuberant   B. chaotic   C. urgent

_____ 8. limitations

A. eruptions   B. restrictions   C. resumptions

_____ 9. exploded

A. urged   B. concerned   C. erupted

_____ **10.** pleaded with; coaxed

A. erupted   B. concerned   C. urged

Practice Eight:
Context Clues

Read the following selection. <u>Underline</u> the context clues that help you to understand the meaning of each CAPITALIZED word.

Freaky Science Fiction

Are you a science fiction freak? Is your secret wish to be the LEGENDARY superman or the captain of an interplanetary space ship? Do you want a clashing ENCOUNTER with a calculating COMPUTER? Will this machine plot and CONSPIRE against you? Do you silently enjoy tormenting, HARROWING tales? Does the unknown OCCULT keep you glued to your seat? Are you baffled by the sly SCHEMES of the hellishly NOTORIOUS Dracula? Do you gasp at the CRITICAL, dangerous moment that is threatening and MENACING the hero?

Join the club. You, too, are a real science fiction freak!

Practice Nine:
Definitions

Listed below are definitions for each CAPITALIZED word used in Practice Eight. Write the CAPITALIZED word that best matches each definition. There is a clue after each definition. Remember to look for the context clues in Practice Eight.

Words	*Definitions*
_____	**1.** threatening; endangering (m-)
_____	**2.** unknown; mysterious, hidden (o-)
_____	**3.** based on old stories; superhuman; mythical; heroic (l-)
_____	**4.** terrifying; frightening; tormenting (har-)
_____	**5.** underhanded plans (sche-)
_____	**6.** famous or well known for evil reasons; infamous (n-)
_____	**7.** dangerous, serious, risky (cr-)

_____ **8.** calculator; automatic elec-
tronic machine (comp-)

_____ **9.** meeting; clash; battle (en-)

_____ **10.** plot against; connive (con-)

Practice Ten:
Matching

Write the word that best matches each definition.

	Definitions	*Words*
_____ **1.**	meeting	**a.** legendary
_____ **2.**	calculator	**b.** menacing
_____ **3.**	dangerous	**c.** encounter
_____ **4.**	heroic; mythical	**d.** harrowing
_____ **5.**	unknown; mysterious	**e.** scheme
_____ **6.**	frightening	**f.** conspire
_____ **7.**	plot against	**g.** computer
_____ **8.**	plan	**h.** occult
_____ **9.**	endangering	**i.** notorious
_____ **10.**	famous in an evil way	**j.** critical

Practice Eleven:
Using the Words

Write the CAPITALIZED word that correctly answers each of the following questions.

_____ **1.** Superman performs many heroic deeds. Is he a LEGENDARY or a MENACING hero?

_____ **2.** Would an attack on a major city be OCCULT or MENACING?

_____ **3.** Your favorite character on television was in an automobile accident. Would this be a HARROWING or SCHEMING experience?

_____ **4.** Do the SCHEMES or the COMPUTERS of science fiction writers have to be almost believable?

_____ **5.** A person is trying to take over a space ship. Would he CONSPIRE or COMPUTER against the captain of the ship?

_____ **6.** The rocket ship is going to another galaxy. Will it do this with the help of ENCOUNTERS or COMPUTERS?

_____ **7.** The hero reported moaning sounds and misty, floating shapes. Did he suspect the OCCULT or the COMPUTER?

_____ **8.** The foreign agent is famous for his ability to steal classified, secret information. Is the agent CRITICAL or NOTORIOUS?

_____ **9.** A cliff-hanger stops at the crucial, dangerous part of the story. Does it stop at the CRITICAL or the LEGENDARY point?

_____ **10.** Do you enjoy the COMPUTERS or the ENCOUNTERS of space heroes with interplanetary villains?

Practice Twelve:
Multiple Choice

Next to each number write the letter of the best definition.

	Words	*Definitions*
_____	**1.** COMPUTERS	A. calculators
		B. generators
		C. carburetors
_____	**2.** CONSPIRE	A. plot against
		B. plan openly
		C. speak out
_____	**3.** CRITICAL	A. settled
		B. safe
		C. dangerous
_____	**4.** ENCOUNTER	A. agreement
		B. union
		C. meeting
_____	**5.** HARROWING	A. calming
		B. memorable
		C. terrifying
_____	**6.** LEGENDARY	A. superhuman
		B. unknown
		C. genuine
_____	**7.** MENACING	A. reasoning
		B. threatening
		C. sensing
_____	**8.** NOTORIOUS	A. virtuous
		B. infamous
		C. moral
_____	**9.** OCCULT	A. plain
		B. definite
		C. mysterious
_____	**10.** SCHEMES	A. plans
		B. good humor
		C. poor humor

Practice Thirteen:
Word Families

Here are some more new words. They were formed by adding suffixes or taking away suffixes from the words listed. The new words are CAPITALIZED, and the following abbreviations are used: v. (verb), n. (noun), and adj. (adjective).

1. notorious-n.
NOTORIETY-n.   being well known for bad deeds
2. critical-adj.
CRITICIZE-v.   disapprove of; find fault with
3. legendary-adj.
LEGEND-n.   a story from the past whose truth cannot be checked
4. occult-n.
OCCULTIST-n.   one who believes in supernatural powers and ways of controlling them
5. conspire-v.
CONSPIRATOR-n. plotter; spy
6. schemes-n.
SCHEMING-adj.   underhanded planning
7. harrowing-adj.
HARROW-v.   torment; worry
8. menacing-v.
MENACE-n.   a danger; a threat
9. encounter-n.
ENCOUNTER-v.   meet; come upon
10. computer-n.
COMPUTE-v.   reckon; figure; add up

Can you use these new words? Write the word needed to complete each of the following sentences.

1. In the last episode of the TV show, bandits worried and tormented the villagers. They continued to _____ the people until the police put the robbers in jail.

2. In most science fiction stories a large calculating machine is able to _____ distances.

3. The leader of the robots has given many unpopular orders. His assistants often _____ his judgment.

4. The _____ of Frankenstein's monster has been shown on TV many times.

5. The villain is an _____ whose supernatural powers cause people to fear him.

6. Science fiction stories have characters who are sly and tricky. Their _____ ways cause trouble for others.

7. Mata Hari was a famous spy, a _____ who stole secrets from the enemy.

8. The scientist was completely mad. He was a _____ to society.

9. The captain will have to change the flight plan. If the rocket travels in that direction it will _____ a UFO.

10. In the last TV episode the gang broke every window on Main Street because they had a craze for _____.

Practice Fourteen;
Review

In this practice the definition has been given to you. Has word A, B, or C been defined? Write the defined word on the line to the left.

_____ **1.** calculator

A. occult   B. encounter   C. computer

_____ **2.** meeting

A. scheme   B. computer   C. encounter

_____ **3.** threatening

A. menacing   B. conspire   C. critical

_____ **4.** tormenting

A. scheme   B. harrowing   C. menacing

_____ **5.** plot against

A. conspire   B. encounter   C. computer

_____ **6.** underhanded plans

A. occult   B. schemes   C. encounters

_____ **7.** unknown; hidden; mysterious

A. notorious   B. critical   C. occult

_____ **8.** heroic; superhuman

A. legendary   B. notorious   C. computer

—————————————————— **9.** infamous; famous for evil reasons

         A. critical   B. legendary   C. notorious

—————————————————— **10.** dangerous or risky

         A. occult   B. legendary   C. critical

Practice Fifteen:
Word Puzzle

Word puzzles are everywhere. They appear in our newspapers, in our favorite magazines, on television, and on place mats at the local diner. The ten listed words in the puzzle go in any direction. You will find their definitions on the next page. Circle the word as you find it; one word may overlap another. Then write each word next to the correct definition.

D	A	Q	R	I	V	C	Z	U	M	P	D	O
R	E	L	U	B	M	H	U	R	I	E	I	N
K	X	M	C	E	V	A	N	G	J	L	S	Z
P	U	R	O	S	R	O	M	E	B	R	P	O
E	B	E	N	N	E	S	K	N	M	O	E	M
K	E	S	C	H	S	E	C	T	O	N	R	N
L	R	T	E	W	T	T	B	U	Q	K	S	R
J	A	R	R	K	R	E	R	U	P	T	E	D
H	N	A	N	D	I	S	E	A	Y	P	X	I
E	T	I	E	D	C	Z	S	K	T	T	O	D
I	G	N	D	N	T	A	U	P	Z	O	Q	P
U	F	T	E	X	I	J	M	Q	P	P	R	W
T	W	F	P	M	T	O	E	V	U	R	W	S

	Words	*Clues*
_____		**1.** burst forth
_____		**2.** calling for immediate attention
_____		**3.** confine
_____		**4.** protesters
_____		**5.** confusion
_____		**6.** take up again
_____		**7.** scatter; disband
_____		**8.** lively; excited
_____		**9.** limiting; repressing
_____		**10.** troubled; worried

Practice Sixteen:
Antonyms

ANTONYMS are words that are OPPOSITE or NEAR OPPOSITE to other words. You are given the opposite or near opposite definition to your listed word. Can you pick out the correct listed word that is opposite in meaning? Write the word next to its antonym.

	Antonym	*Word*
_____	**1.** good, decent (not evil)	**a.** legendary
		b. notorious
_____	**2.** protect	**c.** occult
_____	**3.** safe (not risky)	**d.** scheming
_____	**4.** factual; historical	**e.** menace
_____	**5.** plain; clear	**f.** critical
_____	**6.** honest (not underhanded)	

Practice Seventeen:
Search and Find

Here are TV terms. Use your dictionary to find their meanings. Then write sentences with the words.

1. variety show   **5.** newscaster

2. hero   **6.** setting

3. host   **7.** editor

4. network

STEP ELEVEN: **You and Politics**

Everyone knows the word POLITICS means the science of government. But did you know it also means scheming for power?

The word POLITICIAN is equally familiar: a person active in politics, frequently one elected to a government job. Here again, the word may be used in a negative way to indicate a person who schemes to advance only himself, his own views, or his own party.

Government and politicians affect our lives in many ways. Therefore, it is important that we clearly understand the words they use and the messages they are sending to us. Only by knowing what they're talking about can we react intelligently.

**Practice One:
Context Clues**

Read the following selection. Notice the CAPITALIZED words. Underline the context clues that help you understand their meanings.

Political Candidates

Each year at election time we must decide which CANDIDATES we are going to vote for. Since these people think differently about problems, we classify them according to their ideas and the solutions they offer.

The person who avoids the extremes of political and social measures we label MODERATE or middle-of-the-roader. This person occupies the central position.

From this middle position, we move to the right to describe those who resist change to varying degrees. The CONSERVATIVE likes things the way they are. He wants to keep existing conditions and institutions.

Farther to the right is the REACTIONARY. This individual wants to move backward to an earlier and usually outdated political or social order. He or she is the person who would do away with such programs as Social Security.

Moving again from the central or moderate position this time to the left, we have the LIBERAL. This is the person who supports and works for those changes in government that will provide the individual with more economic freedom and more participation in what government does.

170

The RADICAL is the farthest away from the moderate or traditional position. This person wants to make extreme changes in existing conditions. In addition, the radical usually wants changes made quickly and, therefore, supports extreme measures to achieve these political goals.

Candidates for a political job state opinions dealing with many areas of our country. They express their views about the URBAN area and problems dealing with city life. They discuss the SUBURBAN area and conditions in the region just outside of the city. Finally, they offer opinions about the RURAL area and the problems of farmers and others who live in this section.

To make an intelligent decision, we voters must examine the candidate's CREDENTIALS. These will help us to decide whether a person is qualified to be elected to a political job.

Practice Two:
Definitions

Listed below are definitions for each CAPITALIZED word used in Practice One. Write the CAPITALIZED word that best matches each definition. There is a clue after each definition. Remember to look for the context clues in Practice One.

Words

_____

_____

_____

_____

_____

_____

Definitions

1. written proof of qualifications or experience; qualifications of people running for office (cre-)

2. a person who likes things the way they are; a person who opposes major changes (con-)

3. a person running for an elected office; an office seeker (can-)

4. a person who wants to move back to things as they were, to an outdated political order; a right-winger (re-)

5. a person who wants change, reforms, progress to improve conditions (li-)

6. having to do with city life; metropolitan (ur-)

_____   **7.** a person who wants drastic reforms; extremist; left-winger,
rebel; revolutionary (rad-)

_____   **8.** having to do with the country
or farming; rustic (rur-)

_____   **9.** a person who likes careful, reasonable changes and avoids ex-
tremes; a middle-of-the-roader
(mod-)

_____   **10.** just outside the city (su-)

Practice Three:
Matching

Write the word that best matches each definition.

	Definitions	**Words**
_____	**1.** a person who wants to move toward an earlier political and social order	**a.** candidate
		b. urban
		c. liberal
		d. rural
_____	**2.** a person who wants progress and reform; a progressive	**e.** credentials
		f. conservative
_____	**3.** an office seeker; a person voters will decide upon	**g.** reactionary
		h. moderate
		i. radical
_____	**4.** a person who likes things as they are	**j.** suburban
_____	**5.** dealing with city life	
_____	**6.** a person who wants rapid, violent changes	
_____	**7.** a person who avoids extremes	

_____ **8.** having to do with
farming; country life

_____ **9.** just outside the city;
the outskirts

_____ **10.** proof of
qualifications

Practice Four:
Using the Words

Write the CAPITALIZED word that correctly answers each of the following questions.

_____ **1.** You live on a large Texas ranch. Do you live in a RURAL or URBAN area?

_____ **2.** You are running for mayor. Are you a CANDIDATE or a CONSERVATIVE?

_____ **3.** You live in an apartment in New York City. Do you live in a RURAL or an URBAN area?

_____ **4.** You like things as they are at this time and do not want any changes. Are you a MODERATE or a CONSERVATIVE?

_____ **5.** If necessary, you favor overthrowing the government to improve living and working conditions. Are you a LIBERAL or a RADICAL?

_____ **6.** You believe that the person running for governor should have ability and experience. Do you believe this person should have good CREDENTIALS or be a good LIBERAL?

_____ 7. The senator favored careful, reasonable changes in the laws of her state. Was she a CONSERVATIVE or a MODERATE?

_____ 8. You believe Social Security, Workmen's Compensation, and income tax should be discontinued. Are you a CONSERVATIVE or a REACTIONARY?

_____ 9. You live in a development of private homes just about ten miles from the closest city. Do you live in an URBAN or SUBURBAN area?

_____ 10. That congressman favors changes in United States laws to improve working conditions and to guarantee equal rights. Is he a LIBERAL or a REACTIONARY?

Practice Five:
Multiple Choice

Write the letter of the definition that best defines each capitalized word.

Words	*Definitions*
_____ **1.** CANDIDATE	A. a speech writer for a political person
	B. a person wanting to hold political office
	C. a person who votes
_____ **2.** CONSERVATIVE	A. a person who wants to go back to things as they were
	B. a person who wants many changes
	C. a person who likes things as they are
_____ **3.** CREDENTIALS	A. voters
	B. qualifications
	C. people running for office

_____ **4.** LIBERAL

    A. a person who wants change to improve conditions

    B. a person who does not want any changes

    C. a person who wants changes to make things the way they were

_____ **5.** MODERATE

    A. a person who likes many changes

    B. a person who likes careful, reasonable changes

    C. a person who likes things as they were

_____ **6.** REACTIONARY

    A. one who wishes to go back to things as they were

    B. one who wishes to have many radical changes

    C. one who does not want any changes

_____ **7.** RADICAL

    A. a person who wants extreme changes

    B. a person who wants no changes

    C. a person who wants careful changes

_____ **8.** RURAL

    A. farm; country

    B. outside the city

    C. city

_____ **9.** SUBURBAN

    A. city

    B. farm and country

    C. just outside the city

_____ **10.** URBAN

    A. farm; country

    B. city

    C. just outside the city

Practice Six:
Word Families

Our vocabulary can be expanded by adding new meanings to familiar words and by adding or subtracting word endings. Here are some new entries for your word bank. The new words are CAPITALIZED, and the following definitions are used: v. (verb), n. (noun), and adj. (adjective).

1. candidate-n.
    CANDID-adj.   frank; open; honest
2. conservative-n.
    CONSERVE-v.   protect from loss or waste; save
    CONSERVATION-n.   careful protection from loss or waste; planned management
3. credentials-n.
    CREDENCE-n.   belief; faith; trust

4. liberal-n.
   LIBERAL-adj.   generous; plentiful
5. moderate-n.
   MODERATOR-n.   a chairperson of a meeting or discussion
6. radical-n.
   RADICAL-adj.   severe; extreme; drastic; harsh
7. reactionary-n.
   REACT-v.   respond to something
8. suburban-adj.
   SUBURB-n.   a town or district just outside a city
9. urban-adj.
   URBANITE-n.   a person living in the city

Can you use these new words? Write the word needed to complete each of the following sentences.

1. The voters gave _____ donations so that their candidate had enough money to appear on TV.

2. The_____ will explain the rules for the debate.

3. A person voting in the city considers himself an _____

_____.

4. A _____ person will tell the voters where he got the money for his political campaign.

5. The_____ just to the north of the city sometimes controls the vote.

6. Making speeches against your own party's candidate for President is a _____ move for a politician to make.

7. A voter should not give _____ to rumors.

8. The candidate stressed_____ of fuel oil so that our supply would last through the winter.

9. Candidates must _____ energy during a political campaign or they will run out of physical strength.

10. The candidate did not_____ when told he had lost the election.

Practice Seven:
Review

In this practice the definition has been given to you. Has word A, B, or C been defined? Write the defined word on the line to the left.

_____   **1.** written proof of experiences

A. candidates   B. credentials

C. conservatives

_____   **2.** any person who runs for an office

A. conservative   B. moderate

C. candidate

_____   **3.** a person who wants careful, reasonable changes

A. reactionary   B. moderate   C. radical

_____   **4.** pertaining to city life

A. rural   B. suburban   C. urban

_____   **5.** a person who likes things as they are

A. conservative   B. liberal   C. reactionary

_____   **6.** just outside the city

A. rural   B. suburban   C. urban

_____   **7.** a person who wants to go back to things as they were

A. conservative   B. liberal   C. reactionary

_____   **8.** a person who wants to improve living and working conditions

A. reactionary   B. conservative   C. liberal

_____   **9.** pertaining to the farm area

A. rural   B. suburban   C. urban

_____   **10.** a person who wants rapid, extreme changes

A. reactionary   B. moderate   C. radical

Practice Eight:
Context Clues

Read the following selection. Notice the CAPITALIZED words. Underline the context clues to help you understand their meanings.

A Two-Party System

Our government is basically a two-party system made up of the Democratic and Republican parties. Both parties hold a CONVENTION, a national meeting, once a year to select people to run for political office. Each area or PRECINCT is represented. These DELEGATES select candidates to run for the political jobs that have to be filled.

A successful candidate needs a PLURALITY of the votes over the next highest candidate. Since some jobs may be sought by several popular people, a person may win by only a small MARGIN. Even one vote is enough to determine who will be chosen the party's candidate. Usually the INCUMBENT, the person in office, is chosen to run for a second term. The party then ENDORSES the person and supports the CAMPAIGN for reelection.

In addition to choosing candidates, the party decides upon a PLATFORM, a statement of policies and principles that will be used to get its candidates elected. This platform states the political ideas, laws, and reforms that the party believes should be emphasized. The party then maps out a STRATEGY, a plan of action, to achieve the goal of victory at election time.

Practice Nine:
Definitions

Listed below are definitions for each capitalized word in Practice Eight. Write the CAPITALIZED word that best matches each definition. There is a clue after each definition to help you match words and meanings. Remember to look for the context clues in Practice Eight.

Words	*Definitions*
_____	1. gives approval to; supports (e-)
_____	2. planned actions to elect a candidate (c-)
_____	3. representatives (d-)
_____	4. amount just above or just below amount needed (m-)
_____	5. a plan of action (s-)
_____	6. political party's statement of election plans; set of plans and principles (pl-)
_____	7. meeting of members from different places; gathering; conference (con-)
_____	8. a district; an election area (pre-)

_____   **9.** at least one vote more than the number of votes cast for any other candidate (pl-)

_____   **10.** a person in office; currently in office (in-)

Practice Ten:
Matching

Write the word which best matches each definition.

	Definitions	*Words*
_____	**1.** appeal for votes	**a.** delegates
_____	**2.** the person hold-ing an office	**b.** plurality
_____	**3.** political party's ideas	**c.** margin
_____	**4.** meeting	**d.** incumbent
_____	**5.** a voting district	**e.** platform
_____	**6.** give approval	**f.** strategy
_____	**7.** representatives	**g.** convention
_____	**8.** the amount just beyond what is needed	**h.** precinct
_____	**9.** more votes than anyone else	**i.** endorse
_____	**10.** plan of action	**j.** campaign

Practice Eleven:
Using the Words

Write the CAPITALIZED word that correctly answers each of the following questions.

_____   **1.** You are running for office and have promised the voters that you will fight for decent hous-ing. Is this a CAMPAIGN

—————————————————

—————————————————

—————————————————

—————————————————

—————————————————

—————————————————

—————————————————

promise or an INCUMBENT promise?

2. You have been appealing for votes in different ways. Have you been using MARGIN or STRATEGY to win the election?

3. The honesty of a person running for office is in question. Is it likely that voters will ENDORSE or CAMPAIGN such a candidate?

4. Your candidate won 75 percent of all the votes. Did that person win by a large CONVENTION or a large MARGIN?

5. The present governor wishes to be reelected. Is the governor an INCUMBENT or a PRECINCT?

6. A candidate has listed many plans he expects to carry out. Has this person presented a PLURALITY or a PLATFORM?

7. A candidate is running against three other people. Can this person win by a PLURALITY or a CONVENTION?

8. You will cast a vote on election day. Will you go to your local voting PLATFORM or PRECINCT?

_____   **9.** Chicago, Illinois, has many large hotels. Would a major political party hold a CONVENTION or a PLATFORM in such a city?

_____   **10.** Four people have been sent to a national meeting to represent an area of the country. Are they CONVENTIONS or DELEGATES?

Practice Twelve:
Multiple Choice

Write the letter of the definition that best defines each CAPITALIZED word.

<table>
<tr><td>*Words*</td><td>*Definitions*</td></tr>
<tr><td>_____ **1.** CAMPAIGN</td><td>A. a count to decide the winner</td></tr>
<tr><td></td><td>B. a vote for a candidate</td></tr>
<tr><td></td><td>C. a series of planned actions to elect a candidate</td></tr>
<tr><td>_____ **2.** CONVENTION</td><td>A. a meeting</td></tr>
<tr><td></td><td>B. a written statement</td></tr>
<tr><td></td><td>C. a political promise</td></tr>
<tr><td>_____ **3.** DELEGATES</td><td>A. political jobs</td></tr>
<tr><td></td><td>B. victory speeches</td></tr>
<tr><td></td><td>C. representatives</td></tr>
<tr><td>_____ **4.** ENDORSES</td><td>A. withdraws support</td></tr>
<tr><td></td><td>B. refuses support</td></tr>
<tr><td></td><td>C. gives support</td></tr>
<tr><td>_____ **5.** INCUMBENT</td><td>A. a person running for office for the first time</td></tr>
<tr><td></td><td>B. a person in office</td></tr>
<tr><td></td><td>C. a person who is retiring from office</td></tr>
</table>

_____ **6.** MARGIN   A. an amount that is above or below the amount needed

B. an amount that is exactly one-half

C. an amount that is exactly three-fourths

_____ **7.** PLATFORM   A. a political party's complaint

B. a political party's announcement of election plans and policies

C. a political speech

_____ **8.** PLURALITY   A. the smallest number of votes cast for any candidate

B. at least one vote more than the number of votes cast for any other candidate

C. at least one vote less than the number of votes cast for any other candidate

_____ **9.** PRECINCT   A. an election area or district

B. a political job

C. a national meeting

_____ **10.** STRATEGY   A. a statement

B. a plan of action

C. an achievement

Practice Thirteen:
Word Families

Our vocabulary can be expanded by adding new meanings to familiar words and by adding or subtracting word endings. Here are some new entries for your word bank. The new words are CAPITALIZED, and the following abbreviations are used: v. (verb), n. (noun), and adj. (adjective).

1. convention-n.
CONVENE-v.   assemble; gather
2. delegates-n.
DELEGATION-n.   group of representatives
3. endorse-v.
ENDORSEMENT-n. approval; support
4. margin-n.
MARGINAL-adj.   hardly enough
5. strategy-n.
STRATEGIST-n.   an expert planner

Can you use these new words? From the list that follows select the word needed to complete each of the sentences below.

Word List: campaign, convene, delegation, endorsement, incumbent, marginal, platform, plurality, precinct, strategist.

1. The _____ of senior citizens asked the mayor for more police protection.

2. The president's _____ of our candidate will guarantee his election.

3. The _____ suggested many exciting ideas for the campaign.

4. The chairperson will _____ the meeting by asking the delegates to sit down.

5. The party considered his victory a _____ one since he received barely 50 percent of the vote.

6. He barely won the election by a _____ of the votes.

7. The national committee prepared a _____ which announced their election plans.

8. President Eisenhower was an _____ who chose to run for a second term.

9. _____ promises are sometimes difficult to carry out.

10. The officials of the local _____ send the voting results to the broadcasters.

Practice Fourteen:
Review

In this practice the definition has been given. Has word A, B, or C been defined? Write the defined word on the line to the left.

_____ **1.** gives support

A. delegates   B. endorses   C. conventions

_____ **2.** listing of election plans and policies

A. margin   B. platform   C. precinct

_____ **3.** at least one vote more than the number of

votes cast for any other candidate

A. plurality   B. incumbent   C. campaign

_____ **4.** an amount that is just above or below the

amount needed

A. precinct   B. strategy   C. margin

_____ **5.** a meeting

A. platform   B. plurality   C. convention

_____ **6.** representatives

A. margins   B. precincts   C. delegates

_____ **7.** a person in office

A. incumbent   B. delegate   C. strategist

_____ **8.** a plan of action

A. precinct   B. strategy   C. plurality

_____ **9.** an election area

A. convention   B. margin   C. precinct

_____ **10.** planned actions to elect a candidate

A. campaign   B. precinct   C. incumbent

Practice Fifteen:
Scrambled Words

Can you unscramble these words? They were listed in Practice Six.

_____ **1.** DCNERECE   a belief, a trust

_____ **2.** AERTC   respond to something

_____ **3.** RETARDOMO   a chairperson

_____ **4.** REVENOSC   to save

_____ **5.** NDADIC   open, honest

_____ **6.** UBSURB   district just outside a
                                                city

_____ **7.** BARELIL   generous; plentiful

_____ **8.** DACILAR   left-wing; rebel

_____ **9.** VECNOTANOISR   careful protection
                                                from waste

_____ **10.** RABNU   citylike

STEP TWELVE: **You and Your Money**

Practice One:
Context Clues

Read the following selection. Underline the context clues that help you to understand the meaning of each CAPITALIZED word.

Money Makes Money

How can your money make money? You can realize a handsome profit by ACCELERATING the rate at which your ASSETS grow. First, take the INITIAL step by asking for the help of a CONSULTANT at your local bank. This person will explain the quarterly interest rates that will add money to your account. While your INVESTMENT is growing, you can divide and DIVERSIFY those funds. One way is through the purchase of a six-month bank CERTIFICATE which YIELDS more profit in a shorter period of time. Be AGGRESSIVE and forceful in money matters. Advance your FINANCIAL standing and prove that money makes money.

Practice Two:
Definitions

Listed below are definitions for each capitalized word used in Practice One. Write the CAPITALIZED word that best matches each definition. There is a clue after each definition. Remember to look for the context clues in Practice One.

Words   *Definitions*

_____   **1.** money put into something such as a business to make a profit (inv-)

_____   **2.** document; written or printed statement giving official information (c-)

_____   **3.** first; beginning; starting; introductory (in-)

_____   **4.** produces; provides, gives (y-)

_____   **5.** hastening; speeding up, hurry-
                                           ing up (ac-)

_____   **6.** an expert called on for advice
                                           or opinion (con-)

_____   **7.** bold, forceful (ag-)

_____   **8.** wealth; money; valuable pos-
                                           sessions (as-)

_____   **9.** divide; vary; increase the vari-
                                           ety of (di-)

_____   **10.** having to do with money mat-
                                           ters; fiscal (f-)

Practice Three: Write the word that best matches each definition.
Matching

	Definitions	**Words**
_____	**1.** money put into business	**a.** accelerating
_____	**2.** produces; gives	**b.** initial
_____	**3.** speeding up	**c.** assets
_____	**4.** wealth; money	**d.** yields
_____	**5.** first; beginning	**e.** diversify
_____	**6.** having to do with money matters	**f.** aggressive
_____	**7.** expert; adviser	**g.** certificate
_____	**8.** vary; divide; spread out	**h.** consultant
_____	**9.** bold; forceful	**i.** investment
_____	**10.** document; official written statement	**j.** financial

Practice Four:
Using the Words

Write the CAPITALIZED word that correctly answers each of the following questions.

_____

1. Your friend has no money. Is that person in FINANCIAL or in INITIAL trouble?

_____

2. A man owns real estate which totals ten million dollars. Are his CERTIFICATES or ASSETS high?

_____

3. You need advice. Would you go to an INVESTMENT or to a CONSULTANT?

_____

4. Things cost more each time you go shopping. Is this rise in prices ACCELERATING or AGGRESSIVE?

_____

5. You want to be one of the first to buy a new stock. Do you want to be an INITIAL or an ACCELERATING contributor?

_____

6. You sell some land for twice what it cost you. Would you consider this a good CERTIFICATE or a good INVESTMENT?

_____

7. You have been praised for being forceful in business. Are you considered ACCELERATING or AGGRESSIVE?

_____   **8.** You want to take some of your money out of the savings bank to buy bonds. Do you wish to YIELD or DIVERSIFY your money?

_____   **9.** You need written proof from the bank that you have given them a sum of money. Will they give you a CERTIFICATE or an ASSET?

_____   **10.** You are going to earn 10 percent on a stock you bought. Would you say this stock will YIELD or DIVERSIFY a good return?

Practice Five:
Multiple Choice   Write the letter of the definition that best defines each CAPITALIZED word.

	Words	*Definitions*
_____	**1.** ACCELERATING	A. slowing
		B. hurrying
		C. delaying
_____	**2.** ASSETS	A. valuable things
		B. periods of time
		C. improvements
_____	**3.** INITIAL	A. first
		B. last
		C. middle
_____	**4.** CONSULTANT	A. a person who lends money
		B. a person who guards a bank
		C. an expert called upon for advice

_____ **5.** INVESTMENT   A. a place to keep valuable papers

B. something bought to make a profit

C. a way to keep business records

_____ **6.** DIVERSIFY   A. keep together

B. hold on to

C. divide

_____ **7.** CERTIFICATE   A. official written statement

B. business profit

C. bank account

_____ **8.** YIELDS   A. produces

B. loses

C. uses

_____ **9.** AGGRESSIVE   A. forceful

B. quiet

C. helpful

_____**10.** FINANCIAL   A. having to do with local banks

B. having to do with money matters

C. having to do with shorter periods of time

Practice Six:
Word Families

Here are some new words. They are formed by adding or taking away suffixes from the original words. The new words are CAPITALIZED, and the following abbreviations are used: v. (verb), n. (noun), and adj. (adjective).

1. accelerating-v.
ACCELERATE-v.   go faster
2. aggressive-adj.
AGGRESSION-n.   an unjustified attack
3. assets-n.   plural
ASSET-n.   singular; something useful; an advantage
4. certificate-n.
CERTIFY-v.   state in writing that something is true
5. consultant-n.
CONSULT-v.   look for advice or information
6. diversify-v.
DIVERSITY-n.   variety
7. financial-adj.
FINANCIER-n.   person skilled in money matters

8. initial-adj.
  INITIATE-v.   begin
9. investment-n.
  INVEST-v.   use money to make a profit
10. yields-v.
  YIELDING-adj.   obedient; does not resist

Now can you use these new words? Write the CAPITALIZED word needed to complete each of the following sentences.

1. This record will _____ that you have completed the course.

2. Would you _____ your money in gold or in diamonds?

3. The _____ made more than a million dollars last year.

4. He would never argue. As a result, people took advantage of his _____ nature.

5. Do not _____ quickly when starting a car on ice. Such speed can cause skidding.

6. You will have to _____ the timetable for the next train to New York City.

7. The United Nations discussed Vietnam's _____ against Cambodia.

8. Did you _____ the fight or were you just protecting yourself?

9. Height is an _____ when a person plays basketball.

10. The _____ of the desserts offered made it hard for me to make a choice.

Practice Seven:
Review

In this practice the definition has been given to you. Has word A, B, or C been defined? Write the defined word on the line to the left.

_____ **1.** printed statement giving official information
                           A. asset   B. certificate   C. consultant

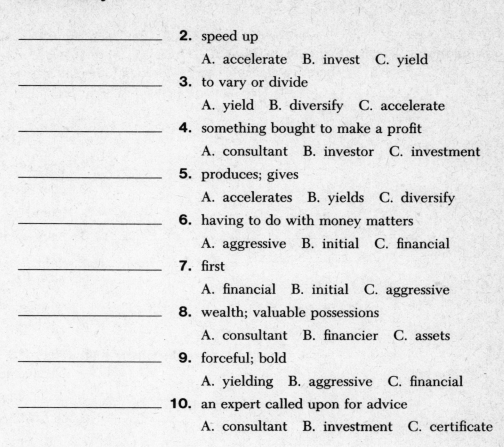

_____ **2.** speed up

     A. accelerate B. invest C. yield

_____ **3.** to vary or divide

     A. yield B. diversify C. accelerate

_____ **4.** something bought to make a profit

     A. consultant B. investor C. investment

_____ **5.** produces; gives

     A. accelerates B. yields C. diversify

_____ **6.** having to do with money matters

     A. aggressive B. initial C. financial

_____ **7.** first

     A. financial B. initial C. aggressive

_____ **8.** wealth; valuable possessions

     A. consultant B. financier C. assets

_____ **9.** forceful; bold

     A. yielding B. aggressive C. financial

_____ **10.** an expert called upon for advice

     A. consultant B. investment C. certificate

Practice Eight:
Context Clues

Read the following paragraph. Underline the context clues that help you to understand the meaning of each CAPITALIZED word.

Inflation and Recession

Are rising prices a problem for you and is INFLATION cramping your style? Do you find that you DISBURSE more money and get less in return? In addition, are you having difficulty paying your financial OBLIGATIONS? Does your income have to be SUBSIDIZED by members of your family because your earnings do not cover your EXPENDITURES? Perhaps the RECESSION has even caused you to lose a job. Many people are beginning to wonder if the downward trend in the ECONOMY will end in a complete DEPRESSION. Has the fear of widespread UNEMPLOYMENT made you think about changing career plans? Although the picture is gloomy, the experts are hopeful. They believe a COMPREHENSIVE program can help solve all of these problems.

Practice Nine:
Definitions

Listed below are definitions for each capitalized word used in Practice Eight. Write the CAPITALIZED word that best matches each definition. There is a clue after each definition. Remember to look for the context clues in Practice Eight.

Words	*Definitions*
_____	1. pay out; distribute (dis-)
_____	2. complete; inclusive; thorough (com-)
_____	3. helped with money (s-)
_____	4. something one must do according to law or because of one's sense of duty; a responsibility (ob-)
_____	5. financial situation or condition; management of the wealth of a country (e-)
_____	6. state of being out of work (un-)
_____	7. bad financial period; period with little business activity, falling prices and wages, and many people out of work (d-)
_____	8. continuing rise in prices (in-)
_____	9. temporary downward trend in business activities (re-)
_____	10. expenses; money spent; paying out (ex-)

Practice Ten:
Matching

Write the word that best matches each definition.

	Definitions	*Words*
_____	1. financial condition	a. unemployment

_____   **2.** state of being out of   **b.** inflation
                               work   **c.** economy

_____   **3.** continuing rise in   **d.** depression
                               prices   **e.** obligations

_____   **4.** distribute; pay out   **f.** disburse

_____   **5.** complete; including a   **g.** comprehensive
                               great deal   **h.** subsidize

_____   **6.** to help or be helped   **i.** recession
                               with money   **j.** expenditures

_____   **7.** temporary falling off
                               of business

_____   **8.** money spent, expenses

_____   **9.** prolonged bad busi-
                               ness period

_____   **10.** responsibilities

Practice Eleven: Write the CAPITALIZED word that correctly answers each of the follow-
Using the Words   ing questions.

_____   **1.** As a paymaster you are respon-
                               sible for giving workers their
                               paychecks. Do you SUBSIDIZE
                               or DISBURSE their salaries?

_____   **2.** The bank offers a complete
                               plan for saving money. Is it a
                               COMPREHENSIVE plan or an
                               ECONOMY plan?

_____   **3.** Last year many people were
                               out of work. Was UNEMPLOY-
                               MENT or were EXPENDI-
                               TURES at an all-time high?

_____   **4.** The cost of things continues to
                               rise. Is this condition DE-
                               PRESSION or INFLATION?

_____

5. The financial condition of the country is sound. Would you say the DEPRESSION or the ECONOMY is in good shape?

_____

6. From 1929 through 1939 our country had less business activity and more people out of work than ever before. Were we in a DEPRESSION or in an INFLATION?

_____

7. Many programs in our country receive money from the federal government. Does the government DISBURSE or SUBSIDIZE these programs?

_____

8. There is a temporary falling off of business activity. Are we in a RECESSION or DEPRESSION?

_____

9. John is spending more than he is earning. Is he running into difficulty with his UNEMPLOYMENT or with his EXPENDITURES?

_____

10. You have a large bill to pay at the end of the month. Do you have an OBLIGATION or an INFLATION?

Practice Twelve:
Multiple Choice

Write the letters of the definition that best defines each CAPITALIZED word.

Words	_Definitions_
_____ **1.** INFLATION	A. continuing fall in prices
	B. no price movement
	C. continuing rise in prices

_____ **2.** DISBURSE   A. pay out

                                           B. receive in payment

                                           C. find money

_____ **3.** OBLIGATIONS   A. responsibilities

                                           B. difficulties

                                           C. objections

_____ **4.** SUBSIDIZE   A. help or assist with money

                                           B. take money away

                                           C. put money in bank

_____ **5.** EXPENDITURES   A. income

                                           B. profit

                                           C. expenses

_____ **6.** RECESSION   A. downward trend in business activity

                                           B. upward turn in business action

                                           C. prosperity

_____ **7.** ECONOMY   A. wasteful condition

                                           B. financial condition

                                           C. unwise condition

_____ **8.** DEPRESSION   A. bad financial period

                                           B. good financial period

                                           C. average financial period

_____ **9.** UNEMPLOYMENT   A. working

                                           B. being out of work

                                           C. being hired for work

_____ **10.** COMPREHENSIVE   A. complete

                                           B. limited

                                           C. narrow

Practice Thirteen:
Word Families

      Here are some more new words. They were formed by adding suffixes or taking away suffixes from words listed. The new words are CAPITALIZED, and the following abbreviations are used: v. (verb), n. (noun), and adj. (adjective).

     1. comprehensive-adj.
         COMPREHEND-v.   understand

2. depression-n.
 DEPRESSED-adj.   1. sad and gloomy
                  2. pressed down

3. disburse-v.
 DISBURSEMENT-n.   money paid out

4. economy-n.
 ECONOMIST-n.   an expert who deals with the problems of finance, taxation, labor, etc.

5. expenditure-n.
 EXPEND-v.   spend; use up

6. inflation-n.
 INFLATE-v.   fill up; increase

7. obligations-n.
 OBLIGED-v.   forced; compelled

8. recession-n.
 RECESS-n.   a pause; time-out

9. subsidize-v.
 SUBSIDY-n.   a grant or gift, especially of money

10. unemployment-n.
 UNEMPLOYED-adj.   not having a job or any way to earn money

Can you use these new words? Write the CAPITALIZED word needed to complete each of the following sentences.

1. It is the job of the _____ to try to solve the country's financial problems.

2. He lost his job six months ago and has been _____ ever since.

3. The _____ from the state government helps to pay school district expenses.

4. Everyone was _____ by the sad news.

5. The judge declared a _____ for the holidays.

6. I was _____ to do the job because of the contract I had signed.

7. How much time and money did you _____ on that project?

8. My bicycle tire is flat. Please _____ it for me.

9. That is the last _____ I have to make. Now all my bills are paid.

10. The UN delegate was speaking in Greek; therefore, we could not _____ his message.

Practice Fourteen:
Review

In this practice the definition has been given to you. Has word A, B, or C been defined? Write the defined word on the line to the left.

_____ **1.** aid with a gift of money

A. comprehend   B. subsidize   C. inflate

_____ **2.** payments; money spent

A. expenditures   B. inflation   C. economy

_____ **3.** state of being out of work

A. depression   B. recession   C. unemployment

_____ **4.** things one must do according to law or according to one's sense of duty

A. expenditures   B. obligations   C. subsidize

_____ **5.** financial condition

A. recession   B. depression   C. economy

_____ **6.** continuing rise in prices

A. inflation   B. recession   C. economy

_____ **7.** pay out; give out in payment

A. recess   B. inflate   C. disburse

_____ **8.** temporary falling off of business activity

A. depression   B. inflation   C. recession

_____ **9.** period marked by little business activity and a great number of people out of work

A. depression   B. recession   C. inflation

_____ **10.** complete; thorough

A. disburse   B. comprehensive   C. obligation

Practice Fifteen:
Crossword Puzzle

All the words defined below can be found in Step Twelve.

Across

1. wealth
2. produce
5. ask advice of
6. forceful
7. first
8. a person skilled in money matters

Down

1. increasing the speed of
3. put money in business or stocks
4. vary; increase the variety of

Practice Sixteen:
Search and Find

The word YIELD has more than five different meanings. Use your dictionary to write all the definitions listed. Then write an original sentence to illustrate each of these meanings. Remember to include context clues.

Answers to Exercises in Step One: You and Keys for Communication

Practice Four: Definitions

A. 3
B. 4
C. 5
D. 2
E. 1

Practice Six: Definitions

1. baseboard
2. base pay
3. base exchange
4. baseborn
5. baseless

Practice Eight: Definitions—Nouns

1. deference
2. finesse
3. eccentricity
4. discretion
5. chagrin

Practice Nine: Completion—Nouns

1. eccentricity
2. chagrin
3. finesse
4. deference
5. discretion

Practice Eleven: Definitions—More Nouns

1. incredulity
2. pessimism
3. serenity
4. indolence
5. rancor

Practice Twelve: Completion—More Nouns

1. pessimism
2. serenity
3. indolence
4. rancor
5. incredulity

Practice Thirteen: Using the Nouns

1. deference
2. incredulity
3. serenity
4. pessimism
5. chagrin
6. discretion
7. rancor
8. finesse
9. eccentricity
10. indolence

Practice Fourteen: Review of Nouns

1. pessimism
2. rancor
3. incredulity
4. deference
5. eccentricity
6. serenity
7. discretion
8. indolence
9. finesse
10. chagrin

Practice Sixteen: Definitions—Adjectives

1. docile
2. gregarious
3. compatible
4. elated
5. dogmatic

Practice Seventeen: Completion—Adjectives

1. gregarious
2. compatible
3. elated
4. docile
5. dogmatic

Practice Nineteen: Definitions—More Adjectives

1. sullen
2. loquacious
3. perverse
4. impartial
5. pensive

Practice Twenty: Completion—More Adjectives

1. sullen
2. loquacious
3. perverse
4. impartial
5. pensive

Practice Twenty-One: Using the Adjectives

1. pensive
2. sullen
3. loquacious
4. compatible
5. elated
6. docile
7. perverse
8. gregarious
9. impartial
10. dogmatic

Practice Twenty-Two: Review of Adjectives

1. loquacious
2. pensive
3. compatible
4. sullen
5. elated
6. docile
7. perverse
8. dogmatic
9. gregarious
10. impartial

Practice Twenty-Four: Definitions—Verbs

1. retract
2. defer
3. concur
4. accrue
5. rectify

Practice Twenty-Five: Completion—Verbs

1. retract
2. defer
3. accrue
4. concur
5. rectify

Practice Twenty-Seven: More Verbs

1. capitulate
2. allocates
3. mandates
4. alleviate
5. collate

Practice Twenty-Eight: Completion—More Verbs

1. mandates
2. collate
3. allocate
4. capitulate
5. alleviate

Practice Twenty-Nine: Using the Verbs

1. collate
2. accrue
3. rectify
4. alleviate
5. mandate
6. retract
7. capitulate
8. defer
9. allocate
10. concur

Practice Thirty: Review of Verbs

1. alleviate
2. mandate
3. defer
4. capitulate
5. concur
6. accrue
7. collate
8. retract
9. allocate
10. rectify

Answers to Exercises in Step Two: You and Featured Families

Practice One: Adding Suffixes to a Root Word

1. changeable
2. changeability
3. changeableness
4. changeably
5. changeful
6. changeless
7. changeling

Practice Two: Adding Prefixes and Suffixes to a Root Word

1. unchanged
2. unchangeable
3. unchangeability
4. unchanging
5. interchange
6. interchangeable
7. exchange
8. exchangeability
9. exchangeable

Practice Three: Locating Root Words

1. act
2. fair
3. meat
4. pack
5. direct
6. fail
7. like
8. guilt
9. certain
10. care
11. turn
12. ship
13. clear
14. move
15. connect
16. respect
17. frequent
18. comfort
19. probably
20. locate

Practice Four: The Prefix UN-

1. accustomed
2. concerned
3. qualified
4. assisted
5. reasonable

Practice Five: Definitions

1. unaccustomed
2. unassisted
3. unconcerned
4. unqualified
5. unreasonable

Practice Six: Using the Words

1. unconcerned
2. unreasonable
3. unaccustomed
4. unassisted
5. unqualified

Practice Eight: The Prefix MIS-

1. managed
2. treated
3. lead
4. judged
5. inform

Practice Nine: Definitions

1. misinform
2. misjudged
3. mislead
4. mismanaged
5. mistreated

Practice Ten: Substituting Words

1. mislead
2. misinformed
3. misjudged
4. mistreated
5. mismanaged

Practice Eleven: Expanding Your Vocabulary

Answers will vary. Your dictionary is your authority.

Practice Twelve: The Prefix DIS-

1. disappear
2. disadvantage
3. disconnect
4. discontent
5. disobey

Practice Thirteen: Definitions

1. connect
2. disadvantage
3. disobey
4. disappear
5. advantage
6. discontent
7. disconnect
8. appear
9. content
10. obey

Practice Fourteen: Expanding Your Vocabulary

Answers will vary. Your dictionary is your authority.

Practice Fifteen: The Prefixes IL-, IM-, IN-, IR-

1. mature
2. legible
3. regular
4. perfect
5. eligible

Practice Sixteen: Definitions

1. illegible
2. ineligible
3. immature
4. imperfect
5. irregular

Practice Seventeen: Using the Words

1. immature
2. irregular
3. eligible
4. imperfect
5. legible

Practice Eighteen: Expanding Your Vocabulary

Answers will vary. Your dictionary is your authority.

Practice Nineteen: The Prefix CO-

1. exist
2. operate
3. captain
4. author
5. defendant

Practice Twenty: Definitions

1. coauthor
2. cocaptain
3. codefendant
4. coexist
5. cooperate

Practice Twenty-One: Substituting One Word for Many

1. codefendants
2. coauthor
3. coexist
4. cocaptains
5. cooperate

Practice Twenty-Two: The Prefix INTER-

1. lock
2. racial
3. act
4. related
5. national

Practice Twenty-Three: Definitions

1. interact
2. interlock
3. international
4. interracial
5. interrelated

Practice Twenty-Four: Using the Words

1. interrelated
2. international
3. interact
4. interracial
5. interlock

Practice Twenty-Five: Expanding Your Vocabulary

Answers will vary. Your dictionary is your authority.

Practice Twenty-Six: The Prefix PRE-

1. plan
2. judge
3. arrange
4. caution
5. mature

Practice Twenty-Seven: Definitions

1. prearrange
2. precaution
3. prejudge
4. premature
5. preplan

Practice Twenty-Eight: Using the Words

1. premature
2. precaution
3. preplan
4. prejudge
5. prearrange

Practice Twenty-Nine: Expanding Your Vocabulary

Answers will vary. Your dictionary is your authority.

Practice Thirty: The Prefix RE-

1. route
2. cycle
3. insert
4. shape
5. appear

Practice Thirty-One: Definitions

1. reappear
2. recycle
3. reinsert
4. reroute
5. reshape

Practice Thirty-Two: Using the Words

1. reshape
2. reappear
3. recycle
4. reroute
5. reinsert

Practice Thirty-Three: Expanding Your Vocabulary

Answers will vary. Your dictionary is your authority.

Practice Thirty-Four: The Prefix SEMI-

1. invalid
2. permanent
3. final
4. conscious
5. monthly

Practice Thirty-Five: Definitions

1. semiconscious
2. semifinal
3. semi-invalid
4. semimonthly
5. semipermanent

Practice Thirty-Six: Using the Words

1. semipermanent
2. semi-invalid
3. semimonthly
4. semiconscious
5. semifinal

Practice Thirty-Seven: Expanding Your Vocabulary

Answers will vary. Your dictionary is your authority.

Practice Thirty-Eight: The Prefix SUB-

1. normal
2. divide
3. way
4. committee
5. standard

Practice Thirty-Nine: Definitions

1. subcommittee
2. subdivide
3. subnormal
4. substandard
5. subway

Practice Forty: Using the Words

1. subway
2. substandard
3. subdivide
4. subcommittee
5. subnormal

Practice Forty-One: Expanding Your Vocabulary.

Answers will vary. Your dictionary is your authority.

Practice Forty-Two: The Prefix
SUPER-

1. powers   4. natural
2. human   5. sensitive
3. abundant

Practice Forty-Three: Definitions

1. superabundant   4. supernatural
2. supersensitive 5. superpower
3. superhuman

Practice Forty-Four: Using the Words

1. supersensitive 4. superhuman
2. supernatural   5. superabundant
3. superpower

Practice Forty-Five: Expanding Your Vocabulary

Answers will vary. Your dictionary is your authority.

Practice Forty-Six: The Prefix
TRANS-

1. atlantic   4. plant
2. form   5. continental
3. action

Practice Forty-Seven: Definitions

1. transaction   4. transform
2. transcontinental 5. transplant
3. transatlantic

Practice Forty-Eight: Using the Words

1. transplant   4. transform
2. transaction   5. transatlantic
3. transcontinental

Practice Forty-Nine: Expanding Your Vocabulary

Answers will vary. Your dictionary is your authority.

Practice Fifty: Locating Suffixes

1. -able   14. -ive
2. -al   15. -ize
3. -ate   16. -less
4. -ed   17. -ly
5. -er   18. -ment
6. -ful   19. -ness
7. -hood   20. -or
8. -fy   21. -ous
9. -ic   22. -ship
10. -ing   23. -ster
11. -ish   24. -ward
12. -ist   25. -y
13. -ity

Practice Fifty-One: Adding Suffixes

1. comfortable   11. collective
2. accidental   12. centralize
3. acceptance   13. fearless
4. deportation   14. exactly
5. hunted   15. lonely
6. starter   16. achievement
7. sorrowful   17. deafness
8. fishing   18. prosperous
9. heroism   19. troublesome
10. humorist   20. stormy

Practice Fifty-Two: Using Context Clues to Help Select the Correct Form of a Word

1. A. ambitiously   C. demonstra-
   B. ambitious   tion
   C. ambition   6. A. endurance
2. A. assistant   B. endure
   B. assistance   C. endurable
   C. assist   7. A. recurrence
3. A. communica-   B. recurrent
      ble   C. recur
   B. communi-   8. A. resistance
      cate   B. resistant
   C. communica-   C. resist
      tion   9. A. skill
4. A. confident   B. skillfully
   B. confide   C. skillful
   C. confidence   10. A. stylishly
5. A. demon-   B. style
      strate   C. stylish
   B. demonstra-
      tive

Practice Fifty-Three: Definitions

1. communicate
2. demonstrate
3. recur
4. skill
5. assist
6. style
7. resist
8. ambition
9. endure
10. confide

Practice Fifty-Four: Adding Suffixes

1. ambitious
2. assistance
3. communicable
4. confidence
5. demonstration
6. endurance
7. recurrence
8. resistance
9. skillfully
10. stylish

Practice Fifty-Five: Funny Foods

1. money
2. not attainable
3. failure
4. an unwanted problem
5. defective car

6. calm
7. argument
8. crazy
9. money
10. stubborn

Practice Fifty-Six: Some Teasers

1. year
2. tear
3. dear
4. fear
5. hear
6. near
7. gear
8. rear

Practice Fifty-Seven: Words from Words

Answers will vary.

Answers to Exercises in Step Three: You and Compound Companions

Practice One: The Challenge

1. airport
2. anything
3. careless
4. crossroad
5. firehouse
6. kneecap
7. landlord
8. lifeline
9. meanwhile
10. midnight
11. overtime
12. pocketbook
13. payroll
14. playboy
15. quarterback
16. salesman
17. sidewalk
18. timetable
19. truckload
20. throughout

Practice Two: Hidden Compounds

1. seaside
2. showman
3. underfoot
4. eyeball
5. superman
6. workhorse
7. centerpiece
8. weightless
9. wildcat
10. backbone
11. statesman
12. roadrunner
13. fireplace
14. watchword
15. landmark
16. bedbug
17. moonstruck
18. backtrack
19. telltale
20. vineyard

Practice Three: Recognizing a Misfit

1. stormbound
2. backboard
3. treetop
4. greenhouse
5. blackbird
6. workhouse
7. pinup
8. tailspin
9. income
10. salesclerk
11. borderland
12. headline
13. racetrack
14. coverall
15. raincoat
16. homeroom
17. sportscar
18. nighttime
19. playback
20. cardplayer

Practice Four: Interesting Pairs—UP and DOWN

1. upstream
2. downstream
3. downtown
4. uptown
5. downbeat
6. upbeat
7. upwind
8. downwind
9. downstate
10. upstate

Practice Five: Using the Words

1. downstream
2. downtown
3. upstate
4. upbeat
5. downwind

Practice Six: Interesting Pairs—More UP and DOWN

1. downswing	6. downward
2. upswing	7. downstage
3. upgrade	8. upstage
4. downgrade	9. downhill
5. upward	10. uphill

Practice Seven: Using the Words

1. downhill	4. downstage
2. upswing	5. upgrade
3. downward	

Practice Eight: Interesting Pairs—OVER and UNDER

1. underdone	6. overpass
2. overdone	7. overcharge
3. overbid	8. undercharge
4. underbid	9. underrate
5. underpass	10. overrate

Practice Nine: Using the Words

1. underrate	4. underpass
2. overcharge	5. overbid
3. underdone	

Practice Ten: Interesting Pairs—HIGH and LOW

1. high-pressure	6. low-grade
2. low-pressure	7. high-level
3. low-spirited	8. low-level
4. high-spirited	9. highland
5. high-grade	10. lowland

Practice Eleven: Using the Words

1. highland	4. low-pressure
2. low-grade	5. high-level
3. high-spirited	

Practice Twelve: Compound Collectibles

Answers will vary. Your dictionary is your authority.

Practice Thirteen: Colorful Compounds

Answers will vary. Your dictionary is your authority.

Answers to Exercises in Step Four: You and Helpful Histories

Self-Test A:

1. B	6. B
2. A	7. A
3. C	8. B
4. A	9. B
5. C	10. B

Practice One: Definitions

1. tantalize	6. mesmerize
2. titanic	7. masochistic
3. mentor	8. gerrymander
4. nemesis	9. chauvinism
5. sadistic	10. boycott

Practice Two: Matching

1. mentor	6. boycott
2. tantalize	7. mesmerize
3. nemesis	8. sadistic
4. titanic	9. masochistic
5. chauvinism	10. gerrymander

Practice Three: Using the Words

1. yes	6. no
2. yes	7. no
3. no	8. yes
4. yes	9. yes
5. yes	10. no

Practice Four: Word Families

1. titan
2. sadism
3. mesmerism
4. tantalizer
5. masochism

Practice Five: Review

1. B
2. B
3. C
4. A
5. A
6. C
7. B
8. B
9. A
10. A

Self-Test B:

1. B
2. B
3. B
4. A
5. C
6. B
7. A
8. B
9. A
10. C

Practice Six: Definitions

1. labyrinth
2. investigate
3. atlas
4. Achilles' heel
5. Like a Dutch uncle
6. Midas touch
7. baker's dozen
8. sword of Damocles
9. fiasco
10. lethargy

Practice Seven: Matching

1. baker's dozen
2. sword of Damocles
3. lethargy
4. labyrinth
5. investigate
6. atlas
7. Achilles' heel
8. Like a Dutch uncle
9. fiasco
10. Midas touch

Practice Eight: Using the Words

1. yes
2. yes
3. no
4. yes
5. no
6. yes
7. no
8. no
9. no
10. yes

Practice Nine: Completion

1. Achilles' heel
2. lethargy
3. fiasco
4. investigate
5. sword of Damocles
6. Midas touch
7. baker's dozen
8. Like a Dutch uncle
9. atlas
10. labyrinth

Practice Ten: Review

1. B
2. B
3. A
4. C
5. A
6. A
7. C
8. B
9. C
10. B

Practice Eleven: More Histories

Your dictionary is your authority.

Practice Twelve: Rhyming Definitions

1. mesmerize
2. tantalize
3. mentor
4. titan
5. boycott

Answers to Exercises in Step Five: You and Deadly Directions

Practice One: Context Clues

1. DESCRIBE: Tell me exactly what happened.
2. LIST: Mention the things one after another in time order.
3. NAME: Son's friends.
4. MATCH: What the son did—each statement made by the father.
5. ANALYZE: Include all details.
6. DISCUSS: Give me your ideas.
7. JUDGE: Whether the father or the son was wrong.
8. PROVE: Show me the evidence.
9. SUMMARIZE: Be brief.
10. EXPLAIN: Include the reasons for your choice.

Practice Two: Definitions

1. analyze	6. list
2. describe	7. match
3. discuss	8. name
4. explain	9. prove
5. judge	10. summarize

Practice Three: Matching

1. discuss	6. analyze
2. match	7. summarize
3. prove	8. describe
4. list	9. judge
5. name	10. explain

Practice Four: Substituting Words

1. discuss	6. describe
2. analyze	7. name
3. list	8. match
4. judge	9. summarize
5. explain	10. prove

Practice Five: Multiple Choice

1. B	6. A
2. A	7. B
3. C	8. C
4. A	9. A
5. B	10. C

Practice Six: Word Families

1. listing	6. judgment
2. explanation	7. discussion
3. summary	8. nameless
4. matchless	9. analysis
5. description	10. namesake

Practice Seven: Review

1. explain	6. describe
2. judge	7. prove
3. analyze	8. match
4. name	9. discuss
5. summarize	10. list

Practice Eight: Context Clues

1. CITE: Statements from school records.
2. COMPARE: How are they alike?
3. CONTRAST: In what ways are they different? In what ways are they similar?
4. CRITICIZE: Suggest better methods.
5. DEFINE: What does it mean?
6. ENUMERATE: List them one after another in time order.
7. EVALUATE: In your opinion are problems handled well?
8. IDENTIFY: List their names.
9. JUSTIFY: Give several reasons.
10. SOLVE: What is your answer to this problem?

Practice Nine: Definitions

1. cite	6. enumerate
2. compare	7. evaluate
3. contrast	8. identify
4. criticize	9. justify
5. define	10. solve

Practice Ten: Matching

1. compare	6. identify
2. enumerate	7. cite
3. justify	8. solve
4. define	9. criticize
5. evaluate	10. contrast

Practice Eleven: Substituting Words

1. solve	6. contrast
2. identify	7. criticize
3. enumerate	8. evaluate
4. cite	9. justify
5. compare	10. define

Practice Twelve: Multiple Choice

1. C	6. A
2. A	7. B
3. A	8. C
4. B	9. C
5. C	10. A

Practice Thirteen: Word Families

1. critical
2. criticism
3. justification
4. comparable
5. comparison
6. solution
7. identification
8. evaluation
9. definite
10. citation

Practice Fourteen: Review

1. criticize
2. justify
3. cite
4. evaluate
5. contrast
6. identify
7. enumerate
8. solve
9. compare
10. define

Practice Fifteen: Reversals

1. meat—team
2. room—moor
3. tin—nit
4. pin—nip
5. tip—pit
6. top—pot
7. spoons—snoops
8. sinned—Dennis
9. pupils—slip up
10. evil—live

Practice Sixteen: Colorful Expressions

Your dictionary is your authority.

Practice Seventeen: More Colorful Expressions

Answers will vary. Your dictionary is your authority.

Answers to Exercises in Step Six: You and Sports

Practice One: Context Clues

1. DOMINATED: The score is 30–14.
2. ANTICIPATE: The score is 30–14.
3. COMPENSATE: Lack of weight; make up for this disadvantage.
4. CONSISTENTLY: He's done it on every kickoff.
5. PURSUED: Number 22 makes the tackle.
6. DISORIENTED: Confused; he's being helped off the field.
7. SUCCESSION: One right after another.
8. INTERCEPTION: Blue Team's captain grabbed the ball.
9. CONVERSION: The kick is good.
10. CONTENDERS: Neither gives up the fight.

Practice Two: Definitions

1. anticipate
2. compensate
3. consistently
4. contenders
5. conversion
6. disoriented
7. dominated
8. interception
9. pursued
10. succession

Practice Three: Matching

1. dominate
2. interception
3. disoriented
4. anticipate
5. succession
6. contender
7. pursue
8. compensate
9. conversion
10. consistently

Practice Four: Using the Words

1. consistently
2. interception
3. conversion
4. succession
5. anticipate
6. contenders
7. dominated
8. pursued
9. disoriented
10. compensate

Practice Five: Using the Words Again

1. succession
2. interception
3. disoriented
4. consistently
5. anticipate
6. pursued
7. conversion
8. dominated
9. contenders
10. compensate

Practice Six: Multiple Choice

1. B
2. C
3. A
4. A
5. B
6. A

7. A	9. C
8. A	10. B

Practice Seven: Word Families

1. domination	6. consistent
2. contend	7. disorientation
3. successor	8. intercept
4. convert	9. anticipation
5. compensation	10. consistency

Practice Eight: Review

1. compensate	6. disoriented
2. interception	7. contend
3. conversion	8. anticipate
4. pursue	9. succession
5. consistent	10. dominate

Practice Nine: Context Clues

1. OPPONENT: Central High School's varsity team is playing for the county championship; South High School.
2. TENSION: Running high, fear a fight, emotional strain.
3. IMPENDING: Defeat hangs over.
4. PLAGUED: Bothered.
5. INCENTIVE: The spirit to try.
6. EJECTED: Ordered off the field.
7. DEJECTED: Low spirits.
8. ERRED: Bad mistake.
9. DESIGNATED: Picked to bat.
10. PROCLAIMED: Official announcement.

Practice Ten: Definitions

1. dejected	6. incentive
2. designated	7. opponent
3. ejected	8. plagued
4. erred	9. proclaimed
5. impending	10. tension

Practice Eleven: Matching

1. erred	6. tension
2. incentive	7. ejected
3. proclaimed	8. opponent
4. dejected	9. designated
5. plagues	10. impending

Practice Twelve: Using the Words

1. plagued	6. opponent
2. dejected	7. err
3. impending	8. proclaimed
4. designated	9. incentive
5. tension	10. ejected

Practice Thirteen: Multiple Choice

1. C	6. C
2. C	7. B
3. B	8. A
4. B	9. A
5. B	10. A

Practice Fourteen: Word Families

1. error	6. tenseness
2. tense	7. proclamation
3. designation	8. dejection
4. plague	9. errata
5. erroneous	10. ejection

Practice Fifteen: Review

1. impending	6. ejected
2. plagued	7. designated
3. dejected	8. proclaimed
4. tension	9. erred
5. opponent	10. incentive

Practice Sixteen: Context Clues

1. RECRUIT: Good players are always needed.
2. FACTORS: Coach considers; he will notice size and speed.
3. AGILITY: Ease and quickness of movement.
4. STRIDE: Long, helps the player get down court fast.
5. REBOUNDS: Seizing the ball quickly after it hits the backboard.
6. FACILITY: Spot the open forward and use that person.
7. TEMPERAMENT: A good disposition.
8. COMPOSURE: Self-control.
9. FRUSTRATED: Feeling discouraged.
10. CONCENTRATE: Not let his attention wander.

Practice Seventeen: Definitions

1. agility
2. composure
3. concentrate
4. facility
5. factors
6. frustrated
7. rebound
8. recruit
9. stride
10. temperament

Practice Eighteen: Matching

1. facility
2. frustrated
3. recruit
4. temperament
5. rebound
6. stride
7. composure
8. factors
9. concentrate
10. agility

Practice Nineteen: Using the Words

1. stride
2. factors
3. agility
4. temperament
5. concentrate
6. recruit
7. composure
8. rebound
9. frustrated
10. facility

Practice Twenty: Multiple Choice

1. C
2. A
3. A
4. B
5. A
6. C
7. B
8. B
9. A
10. C

Practice Twenty-One: Word Families

1. recruitment
2. frustration
3. concentration
4. agile
5. temperamental
6. recruiter
7. temper
8. compose
9. facilitate
10. agileness

Practice Twenty-Two: Review

1. stride
2. facility
3. rebound
4. composure
5. temperament
6. concentrate
7. factors
8. agility
9. recruit
10. frustrated

Answers to Exercises in Step Seven: You and the Law—Legal Language

Practice One: Context Clues

1. CUSTODY: Sheriff's deputy brought . . . people into the courtroom.
2. INDICTED: Crime; accused.
3. FELONY: Serious crime.
4. MISDEMEANOR: Lesser crime.
5. ARRAIGNMENT: Charged with murder.
6. CIVIL: Not criminal.
7. CONTEMPT: Made threatening remarks.
8. JUDGMENT: $1,000.
9. NEGLIGENCE: Should have provided a protective guard around a dangerous machine.

Practice Two: Definitions

1. negligence
2. contempt
3. felony
4. arraignment
5. civil
6. judgment
7. indicted
8. misdemeanor
9. custody

Practice Three: Matching

1. custody
2. indicted
3. felony
4. misdemeanor
5. contempt
6. negligence
7. arraignment
8. judgment
9. civil

Practice Four: Using the Words

1. arraignment
2. civil
3. contempt
4. custody
5. judgment
6. negligence
7. felony
8. misdemeanor
9. indicted

Practice Five: Multiple Choice

1. B
2. B
3. A
4. B
5. B
6. A
7. C
8. B
9. A

Practice Six: Word Families

1. indictment
2. arraigned
3. custodian
4. neglect
5. judicious
6. civil
7. contemptible
8. felon
9. contempt
10. civilian

Practice Seven: Review

1. negligence
2. indicted
3. misdemeanor
4. contempt
5. felony
6. civil
7. custody
8. judgment
9. arraignment

Practice Eight: Context Clues

1. PERPETRATOR: One . . . charged with robbery.
2. EXTRADITED: From Chicago to New York.
3. JURISDICTION: Chicago . . . no . . . over the case.
4. LARCENY: Stolen $10,000.
5. WAIVED: His right to trial by jury; judge would decide.
6. ASSAULTED: Old man . . . victim of the attack.
7. TESTIFY: Victim . . . against the young person.
8. SWINDLER: Cheated old man out of his life savings.
9. IMPOSTOR: Pretended to be a banker.
10. DEFAULTED: Loan . . . failed to make payments.
11. USURY: Collected illegally high interest.

Practice Nine: Definitions

1. assaulted
2. defaulted
3. extradited
4. impostor
5. jurisdiction
6. larceny
7. perpetrator
8. swindler
9. testify
10. usury
11. waived

Practice Ten: Matching

1. impostor
2. perpetrator

3. testify
4. assault
5. waive
6. jurisdiction
7. swindler
8. default
9. larceny
10. extradite
11. usury

Practice Eleven: Using the Words

1. testify
2. assault
3. jurisdiction
4. default
5. extradited
6. impostor
7. larceny
8. perpetrator
9. swindler
10. usury
11. waive

Practice Twelve: Multiple Choice

1. C
2. A
3. A
4. A
5. B
6. C
7. B
8. C
9. B
10. C
11. C

Practice Thirteen: Word Families

1. usurer
2. testimony
3. extradition
4. defaulter
5. perpetrate

Practice Fourteen: Verb Suffixes

1. swindling
2. extradited
3. testifies
4. defaulting
5. perpetrated

Practice Fifteen: Review

1. waive
2. jurisdiction
3. default
4. extradite
5. impostor
6. testify
7. perpetrator
8. assault
9. larceny
10. usury
11. swindler

Practice Sixteen: Powerful Prefixes

1. disagreement
2. discharged or recharged
3. uncivil
4. proclaimed, reclaimed, disclaimed

5. discount, recount, miscount
6. misjudge
7. illegal
8. misplace, displace, replace
9. misinform
10. retrial

Practice Seventeen: Colorful Expressions

Your dictionary is your authority.

Practice Eighteen: More Colorful Expressions

Your dictionary is your authority.

Answers to Exercises in Step Eight: You and Advertising

Practice One: Context Clues

1. AUTHENTIC: real
2. UNADULTERATED: pure
3. MELLOW: sweet, juicy
4. AMPLE: generous
5. COMPACT: neatly ... closely organized
6. INGENIOUS: skillful, fast
7. SUBSTANTIAL: low prices
8. CORRELATED: decor with atmosphere
9. DISCRIMINATING: those who demand the best
10. UNPARALLELED: best quality ... price

Practice Two: Definitions

1. ingenious
2. mellow
3. discriminating
4. correlated
5. ample
6. authentic
7. substantial
8. unadulterated
9. unparalleled
10. compact

Practice Three: Matching

1. unadulterated
2. substantial
3. unparalleled
4. authentic
5. ample
6. mellow
7. correlated
8. discriminating
9. ingenious
10. compact

Practice Four: Using the Words

1. mellow
2. discriminating
3. correlated
4. substantial
5. authentic
6. unadulterated

7. ample
8. compact
9. ingenious
10. unparalleled

Practice Five: Multiple Choice

1. C
2. A
3. A
4. A
5. B
6. B
7. B
8. C
9. A
10. C

Practice Six: Word Families

1. discrimination
2. parallel
3. substantiate
4. amplify
5. authenticate
6. mellowness
7. correlate
8. amplification
9. discriminate
10. compactor

Practice Seven: Review

1. substantial
2. ample
3. mellow
4. compact
5. unparalleled
6. discriminating
7. ingenious
8. authentic
9. unadulterated
10. correlated

Practice Eight: Context Clues

1. STURDY: strong
2. RESPONSIVE: quick-on-the-pickup
3. EFFICIENT: fast-acting
4. CAPACIOUS: roomy
5. LAVISH: rich
6. FLEXIBLE: easy steering
7. OPULENT: rich
8. UNIQUE: one-of-a-kind

9. RELIABLE: dependable
10. OPTIONAL: additional features to choose

Practice Nine: Definitions

1. lavish
2. sturdy
3. reliable
4. efficient
5. optional
6. flexible
7. unique
8. opulent
9. capacious
10. responsive

Practice Ten: Matching

1. lavish
2. optional
3. efficient
4. reliable
5. sturdy
6. responsive
7. opulent
8. capacious
9. flexible
10. unique

Practice Eleven: Using the Words

1. opulent
2. capacious
3. responsive
4. sturdy
5. reliable
6. efficient
7. lavish
8. optional
9. flexible
10. unique

Practice Twelve: Multiple Choice

1. C
2. A
3. A
4. B
5. B
6. C
7. B
8. A
9. A
10. C

Practice Thirteen: Word Families

1. uniqueness
2. option
3. sturdiness
4. opulence
5. lavishness
6. flexibility
7. capaciousness
8. efficiency
9. response
10. reliability

Practice Fourteen: Antonyms

1. little
2. wasteful
3. required
4. cramped
5. ordinary
6. poor
7. rigid
8. undependable
9. weak
10. slow to answer

Practice Fifteen: Review

1. capacious
2. responsive
3. lavish
4. efficient
5. optional
6. unique
7. opulent
8. flexible
9. reliable
10. sturdy

Practice Sixteen: Antonyms

1. A
2. C
3. B
4. C
5. C
6. B
7. A
8. B
9. C
10. B

Practice Seventeen: Hidden Words

1. discriminate
2. ample
3. correlated
4. parallel
5. authentic
6. compact
7. ingenious
8. mellow
9. substantial
10. unadulterated

Practice Eighteen: Scrambled Words

1. responsive
2. flexible
3. capacious
4. reliable
5. lavish
6. sturdy
7. opulent
8. optional
9. unique
10. efficient

Answers to Exercises in Step Nine: You and Your Health—Medical Language

Practice One: Context Clues

1. INTERNIST: physical examination; doctor discovers a problem, recommends a specialist
2. DERMATOLOGIST: skin rash
3. PODIATRIST: foot problem
4. ORTHOPEDIST: breaks a bone
5. RADIOLOGIST: x-ray information
6. SURGEON: operation is needed
7. PATHOLOGIST: examines the tissues
8. OBSTETRICIAN: expecting a baby
9. PEDIATRICIAN: cares for the child
10. PSYCHIATRIST: emotional problems, not a physical problem

Practice Two: Definitions

1. dermatologist
2. internist
3. obstetrician
4. orthopedist
5. pathologist
6. pediatrician
7. podiatrist
8. psychiatrist
9. radiologist
10. surgeon

Practice Three: Matching

1. dermatologist
2. pediatrician
3. orthopedist
4. surgeon
5. radiologist
6. obstetrician
7. podiatrist
8. psychiatrist
9. pathologist
10. internist

Practice Four: Using the Words

1. pediatrician
2. psychiatrist
3. obstetrician
4. internist
5. pathologist
6. surgeon
7. orthopedist
8. radiologist
9. podiatrist
10. dermatologist

Practice Five: Completion

1. internist
2. psychiatrist
3. obstetrician
4. pediatrician
5. dermatologist
6. podiatrist
7. pathologist
8. orthopedist
9. surgeon
10. radiologist

Practice Six: Multiple Choice

1. C
2. B
3. C
4. C
5. A
6. C
7. C
8. B
9. C
10. B

Practice Seven: Word Families

1. dermatology
2. pathology
3. surgery
4. intern
5. radiology
6. psychiatry
7. pediatrics
8. podiatry
9. orthopedics
10. obstetrics

Practice Eight: Review

1. psychiatrist
2. orthopedist
3. dermatologist
4. pathologist
5. obstetrician
6. pediatrician
7. podiatrist
8. radiologist
9. surgeon
10. internist

Practice Nine: Context Clues

1. DIAGNOSIS: Inform the patient about his health problem
2. CONCUSSION: His head had been hit.
3. LACERATED: Hand; broken glass.
4. INCISION: Cut.
5. ANESTHETIZED: Felt no pain.
6. SUTURED: To close it.
7. COAGULATE: Bleeding from the wound lessened.
8. ANTIDOTE: Fight the snakebite poison.
9. PARALYSIS: Unable to move her legs.
10. CONVALESCENCE: Rapid because she followed the doctor's orders.

Practice Ten: Definitions

1. anesthetized
2. antidote
3. coagulate
4. concussion
5. convalescence
6. diagnosis
7. incision
8. lacerate
9. paralysis
10. suture

Practice Eleven: Matching

1. convalescence	6. incision
2. diagnosis	7. lacerated
3. paralysis	8. concussion
4. coagulate	9. anesthetized
5. antidote	10. sutured

Practice Twelve: Using the Words

1. lacerated	6. coagulated
2. antidote	7. concussion
3. paralysis	8. sutured
4. convalescence	9. incision
5. diagnosis	10. anesthetized

Practice Thirteen: Completion

1. concussion	6. diagnosis
2. coagulate	7. paralysis
3. anesthetized	8. incision
4. sutured	9. convalescence
5. lacerated	10. antidote

Practice Fourteen: Multiple Choice

1. C	6. C
2. B	7. B
3. A	8. C
4. C	9. C
5. B	10. A

Practice Fifteen: Word Families

1. suture	6. diagnose
2. paralyze	7. incise
3. convalescent	8. concussive
4. coagulation	9. laceration
5. anesthesia	10. diagnostic

Practice Sixteen: Review

1. antidote	6. paralysis
2. diagnosis	7. sutured
3. lacerated	8. convalescence
4. incision	9. anesthetized
5. coagulate	10. concussion

Practice Seventeen: Find the Impostors

2, 5, 7, 10 were to be checked.

Practice Eighteen: Medical Miracles

1. PLASTIC SURGEON: One who operates on badly formed or injured parts of the body for cosmetic or restorative reasons.
2. MICROSURGEON: One who operates, with extremely small-sized tools, on the smallest, tiniest portions of the body in order to repair them.
3. VASCULAR SURGEON: One who operates on vessels that carry blood and other fluids through the body in order to repair them.
4. ORTHOPEDIC SURGEON: One who operates on diseased, injured, and deformed bones, joints, muscles, tendons and ligaments in order to repair them.

Practice Nineteen: Same Letters—New Word

1. reward	6. posted, depots
2. trades, daters	7. trader, darter
3. lashes	8. spider
4. lemons	9. nailed, Daniel
5. silver, sliver	10. gateman

Answers to Exercises in Step Ten: You and TV

Practice One: Context Clues

1. ERUPTED: joy . . . victory
2. DEMONSTRATORS: filled the streets . . . crowds
3. EXUBERANT: rejoiced
4. CONCERNED: worried
5. RESTRAINT: stop . . . wild celebrations
6. CHAOS: lack of self-control
7. RESUME: normal activities
8. DISPERSE: told to . . . get off the streets
9. URGED: entire sentence
10. RESTRICTIONS: limit personal freedom

Practice Two: Definitions

1. erupted
2. restraint
3. demonstrators
4. exuberant
5. chaos
6. urged
7. resume
8. disperse
9. concerned
10. restrictions

Practice Three: Matching

1. chaos
2. erupted
3. disperse
4. concerned
5. restraint
6. urged
7. exuberant
8. demonstrators
9. resume
10. restrictions

Practice Four: Using the Words

1. erupted
2. restraint
3. demonstrators
4. exuberant
5. chaos
6. urged
7. concerned
8. resume
9. restrictions
10. disperse

Practice Five: Multiple Choice

1. B
2. A
3. B
4. C
5. A
6. C
7. A
8. C
9. B
10. B

Practice Six: Word Families

1. chaotic
2. urgency
3. exuberance
4. concern
5. restrict
6. demonstrate
7. eruption
8. urgent
9. dispersal
10. resumption

Practice Seven: Review

1. disperse
2. concerned
3. chaos
4. demonstrate
5. resume
6. restraint
7. exuberant
8. restrictions
9. erupted
10. urged

Practice Eight: Context Clues

1. LEGENDARY: Superman
2. ENCOUNTER: clashing
3. COMPUTER: calculating
4. CONSPIRE: plot . . . against
5. HARROWING: tormenting
6. OCCULT: unknown
7. SCHEMES: sly
8. NOTORIOUS: hellishly
9. CRITICAL: dangerous
10. MENACING: threatening

Practice Nine: Definitions

1. menacing
2. occult
3. legendary
4. harrowing
5. schemes
6. notorious
7. critical
8. computer
9. encounter
10. conspire

Practice Ten: Matching

1. encounter
2. computer
3. critical
4. legendary
5. occult
6. harrowing
7. conspire
8. scheme
9. menacing
10. notorious

Practice Eleven: Using the Words

1. legendary
2. menacing
3. harrowing
4. schemes
5. conspire
6. computers
7. occult
8. notorious
9. critical
10. encounters

Practice Twelve: Multiple Choice

1. A
2. A
3. C
4. C
5. C
6. A
7. B
8. B
9. C
10. A

Practice Thirteen: Word Families

1. harrow
2. compute
3. criticize
4. legend
5. occultist
6. scheming
7. conspirator
8. menace
9. encounter
10. notoriety

Practice Fourteen: Review

1. computer	6. schemes
2. encounter	7. occult
3. menacing	8. legendary
4. harrowing	9. notorious
5. conspire	10. critical

Practice Fifteen: Word Puzzle

1. erupted	6. resume
2. urgent	7. disperse
3. restrict	8. exuberant
4. demonstrators	9. restraint
5. chaos	10. concerned

Practice Sixteen: Antonyms

1. notorious	4. legendary
2. menace	5. occult
3. critical	6. scheming

Practice Seventeen: Search and Find

Your dictionary is your authority. Sentences will vary.

Answers to Exercises in Step Eleven: You and Politics

Practice One: Context Clues

1. CANDIDATES: election time; going to vote for
2. MODERATE: avoids extremes . . . middle-of-the-roader
3. CONSERVATIVE: resist change, likes things the way they are
4. REACTIONARY: wants to move backward
5. LIBERAL: supports and works for those changes
6. RADICAL: wants . . . extreme changes, wants changes made quickly; extreme measures
7. URBAN: dealing with city life
8. SUBURBAN: just outside the city
9. RURAL: problems of farmers . . . others who live in this section
10. CREDENTIALS: examine . . . to decide whether a person is qualified

Practice Two: Definitions

1. credentials	6. urban
2. conservative	7. radical
3. candidate	8. rural
4. reactionary	9. moderate
5. liberal	10. suburban

Practice Three: Matching

1. reactionary	6. radical
2. liberal	7. moderate
3. candidate	8. rural
4. conservative	9. suburban
5. urban	10. credentials

Practice Four: Using the Words

1. rural	6. credentials
2. candidate	7. moderate
3. urban	8. reactionary
4. conservative	9. suburban
5. radical	10. liberal

Practice Five: Multiple Choice

1. B	6. A
2. C	7. A
3. B	8. A
4. A	9. C
5. B	10. B

Practice Six: Word Families

1. liberal	6. radical
2. moderator	7. credence
3. urbanite	8. conservation
4. candid	9. conserve
5. suburb	10. react

Practice Seven: Review

1. credentials
2. candidate
3. moderate
4. urban
5. conservative
6. suburban
7. reactionary
8. liberal
9. rural
10. radical

Practice Eight: Context Clues

1. CONVENTION: national meeting
2. PRECINCT: each area ... represented
3. DELEGATES: select candidates
4. PLURALITY: votes over the next highest candidate
5. MARGIN: win by only a small
6. INCUMBENT: person in office
7. ENDORSES: person . . . supports
8. CAMPAIGN: reelection
9. PLATFORM: statement of policies and principles
10. STRATEGY: plan of action

Practice Nine: Definitions

1. endorses
2. campaign
3. delegates
4. margin
5. strategy
6. platform
7. convention
8. precinct
9. plurality
10. incumbent

Practice Ten: Matching

1. campaign
2. incumbent
3. platform
4. convention
5. precinct
6. endorse
7. delegates
8. margin
9. plurality
10. strategy

Practice Eleven: Using the Words

1. campaign
2. strategy
3. endorse
4. margin
5. incumbent
6. platform
7. plurality
8. precinct
9. convention
10. delegates

Practice Twelve: Multiple Choice

1. C
2. A
3. C
4. C
5. B
6. A
7. B
8. B
9. A
10. B

Practice Thirteen: Word Families

1. delegation
2. endorsement
3. strategist
4. convene
5. marginal
6. plurality
7. platform
8. incumbent
9. campaign
10. precinct

Practice Fourteen: Review

1. endorses
2. platform
3. plurality
4. margin
5. convention
6. delegates
7. incumbent
8. strategy
9. precinct
10. campaign

Practice Fifteen: Scrambled Words

1. credence
2. react
3. moderator
4. conserve
5. candid
6. suburb
7. liberal
8. radical
9. conservation
10. urban

Answers to Exercises in Step Twelve: You and Your Money

Practice One: Context Clues

1. ACCELERATING: rate
2. ASSETS: grow
3. INITIAL: first
4. CONSULTANT: asking for . . . help
5. INVESTMENT: is growing

6. DIVERSIFY: divide
7. CERTIFICATE: purchase
8. YIELDS: more profit
9. AGGRESSIVE: forceful
10. FINANCIAL: money matters

Practice Two: Definitions

1. investment	6. consultant
2. certificate	7. aggressive
3. initial	8. assets
4. yields	9. diversify
5. accelerating	10. financial

Practice Three: Matching

1. investment	6. financial
2. yields	7. consultant
3. accelerating	8. diversify
4. assets	9. aggressive
5. initial	10. certificate

Practice Four: Using the Words

1. financial	6. investment
2. assets	7. aggressive
3. consultant	8. diversify
4. accelerating	9. certificate
5. initial	10. yield

Practice Five: Multiple Choice

1. B	6. C
2. A	7. A
3. A	8. A
4. C	9. A
5. B	10. B

Practice Six: Word Families

1. certify	6. consult
2. invest	7. aggression
3. financier	8. initiate
4. yielding	9. asset
5. accelerate	10. diversity

Practice Seven: Review

1. certificate	3. diversify
2. accelerate	4. investment

5. yields   8. assets
6. financial   9. aggressive
7. initial   10. consultant

Practice Eight: Context Clues

1. INFLATION: rising prices
2. DISBURSE: more money . . . get less
3. OBLIGATIONS: paying . . . financial
4. SUBSIDIZE: income . . . earnings do not cover
5. EXPENDITURES: earnings do not cover
6. RECESSION: caused you to lose a job; this downward trend
7. ECONOMY: entire sentence
8. DEPRESSION: downward trend in the economy
9. UNEMPLOYMENT: changing career plans; picture is gloomy
10. COMPREHENSIVE: solve all these problems

Practice Nine: Definitions

1. disburse	6. unemployment
2. comprehensive	7. depression
3. subsidized	8. inflation
4. obligation	9. recession
5. economy	10. expenditures

Practice Ten: Matching

1. economy	6. subsidize
2. unemployment	7. recession
3. inflation	8. expenditures
4. disburse	9. depression
5. comprehensive	10. obligations

Practice Eleven: Using the Words

1. disburse	6. depression
2. comprehensive	7. subsidize
3. unemployment	8. recession
4. inflation	9. expenditures
5. economy	10. obligation

Practice Twelve: Multiple Choice

1. C
2. A
3. A
4. A
5. C
6. A
7. B
8. A
9. B
10. A

Practice Thirteen: Word Families

1. economist
2. unemployed
3. subsidy
4. depressed
5. recess
6. obliged
7. expend
8. inflate
9. disbursement
10. comprehend

Practice Fourteen: Review

1. subsidize
2. expenditures
3. unemployment
4. obligations
5. economy
6. inflation
7. disburse
8. recession
9. depression
10. comprehensive

Practice Fifteen: Crossword Puzzle

Across	Down
1. assets	1. accelerating
2. yield	3. invest
5. consult	4. diversify
6. aggressive	
7. initial	
8. financier	

Practice Sixteen: Search and Find

Answers will vary. Your dictionary is your authority.